CHASING THE DRAGON

HARVARD JOURNAL OF ASIATIC STUDIES
2 Divinity Avenue
Cambridge 38, Massachusetts

CHASING THE DRAGON

A Report

on Drug Addiction in Hong Kong

BY

ALBERT G. HESS

1965

THE FREE PRESS

First published in the United States 1965 by

THE FREE PRESS

For information, address:

THE FREE PRESS

A DIVISION OF THE MACMILLAN COMPANY

THE CROWELL-COLLIER PUBLISHING COMPANY

60 Fifth Avenue, New York 11

PRINTED IN THE NETHERLANDS

TO 克方

ACKNOWLEDGMENTS

I wish to express my gratitude for the Ford Foundation's generous support, without which this report could not have been realized.

Next, I would like to offer sincere thanks to all those, both in Asia and in the United States, who so graciously assisted me in my work — from the government officials, judges, physicians and scientists to the slum residents, rooftop dwellers, and, of course, the addicts of Hong Kong. Although space limitations make it impossible for me to mention them all by name, they nonetheless have my sincerest appreciation. I would, however, particularly like to mention the following persons, who responded with patience and generosity to my requests for advice, help, and documentation:

In Hong Kong:

A. A. BAGGOTT, Superintendent of the Narcotics Bureau of the Hong Kong Police; J. M. BAKER, Secretary of the Society for the Aid and Rehabilitation of Drug Addicts; G. W. BONSALL, Deputy Librarian, University of Hong Kong; L. BLUMENTHAL, Senior Superintendent, H.M. Prison (Stanley); JAMES M. N. CHIEN, then Superintendent of the Queen Elizabeth II Youth Center and now Welfare Officer of S.A.R.D.A; Rev. DENHAM CRARY, formerly Welfare Officer, Hong Kong Discharged Prisoners' Aid Society; Rev. AGNAR ESPEGREN, Rennie's Mill; WILLIAM FISH, Senior Officer, Hong Kong Government Information Services; EDWING GAMAREKIAN, Journalist; Dr. LAU MAN PANG, Psychiatrist in charge of the Addiction Treatment Centre at Castle Peak; S. M. LEE, Acting Chief Probation Officer, Kowloon; LEE SIU-CHEUNG, formerly Secretary of the Society for the Aid and Rehabilitation of Drug Addicts; J. C. McDOUALL, Secretary for Chinese Affairs; L. C. MILLINGTON, Chief Preventive Officer; Mrs. R. H. MUNROE, Secretary, Hong Kong Discharged Prisoners' Aid Society; C. JAMES NORMAN, Commissioner of Prisons; PETER OLAES, Staff Writer of the *Hong Kong Tiger Standard*; Dr. OU, Director, Castle Peak Mental Hospital; K. S. C. PILLAI, Editorial Department, *South China Morning Post*; R. S. ROSEN, Superintendent, Victoria Prison; Dr. A. M. RODRIGUES, President of

S.A.R.D.A.; GEORGE W. ROSS, Jr., Director, Foster Parents Plan, Inc.; ANDREW T. ROY, Vice President of Chung Chi College; W. SECRUE, Director of Criminal Investigation, Hong Kong Police; Rev. K. L. STUMPF, Director, Lutheran World Federation, Department of World Service; RICHARD TAPPENDEN, Superintendent, Tai Lam Prison; Dr. P. H. TENG, Director of Medical and Health Services; C. O. TSANG, Welfare Officer, H.K.D.P.A.S.; Dr. W. B. WHITEHILL, Haven of Hope Sanatorium; B. D. WILSON, Chief Assistant Secretary for Chinese Affairs; Dr. P. M. YAP, Director, Mental Health Services; W. T. YOUNG, Assistant Secretary for Chinese Affairs.

In Connection with My Visits to Other Asian Narcotics Centers:

Dr. HASSAU ALI AZARAKHSH, Director General of the Narcotics Department, Ministry of Public Health, Teheran (Iran); SUAHINT BJANIJAKARN, Superintendent, Home for Opium Addicts, Rangsit, Thailand; Dr. LEONG HON KOON, Medical Director of the Singapore Prisons; CARLOS LOPES, Deputy Commissioner of Police, Macau; RICHARD PAW U, Social Affairs Officer with the United Nations, ECAFE, Bangkok; SIGISMONDE REVES, former Commissioner of Police, Macau.

In the United States:

HYMAN H. FRANKEL, Consultant with the President's Committee on Juvenile Delinquency and Youth Crime; Dr. LAWRENCE KOLB, Assistant Surgeon General (Retired); Dr. ALFRED R. LINDESMITH, Indiana University; MILTON G. RECTOR, Executive Director of the National Council on Crime and Delinquency; JOHN C. SCANLON, Director of the Information Center on Crime and Delinquency, NCCD; JACKSON TOBY, Consultant, Youth Development Program, Ford Foundation; Dr. E. LEONG WAY, Chairman, Department of Pharmacology, San Francisco Medical Center, University of California; ARMINE DIKIDJIAN; SHANG-LING FU; JULIA KEH-FANG KAO HESS; LUNG-KING KAO; JIM KEADY; MARY KEADY; ANNA LEE; ADRIENNE MILLER; DORINDA SCHAFER; SALLY SHERWIN; VELMA SKELTON.

A. G. H.

TABLE OF CONTENTS

ILLUSTRATIONS, MAPS AND CHARTS

CHAPTER I

INTRODUCTION

General

From its very beginnings as a British Crown Colony about 122 years ago, the free port of Hong Kong has been closely linked with narcotics. Through its port has passed a large part of the international trade in opiates — a trade that probably became one of the sources for the Colony's reputation as a place of international intrigue. As such, Hong Kong has been the inspiration of countless crime novels, plays, and films; over the years, it has furnished authors and producers with villains and heroes of varying hues, with plots of violence and mystery, with settings of dark narrow alleys, exotic night clubs, Buddhist temples, and Chinese junks.

But Hong Kong's reputation is not limited to the romantic. On a more serious level, its peculiar location at the doorstep of Communist China, its efforts at coping with the grave economic situation created by an overwhelming influx of refugees and a severe shortage of housing have attracted a great deal of attention all over the world.

And then, of course, there is the ever-present narcotics problem. For over a hundred years, Hong Kong has been mentioned again and again whenever the production, traffic, and harmful effects of drugs were discussed. Its name has appeared in countless statistical reports on the import, export, seizure, and consumption of narcotics. Only recently, Hong Kong was mentioned in connection with Red China's alleged attempts at poisoning the Western world through its opium.

As in the United States, "addiction" and "addict" are terms loosely used in Hong Kong to designate the use or user of illegally obtained narcotics. These terms are employed without regard to whether symptoms of addiction (in its strict sense) — physical dependence, tolerance, and psychological dependence — are actually present in the user. As the White House *Ad Hoc* Panel on Drug Abuse recently pointed out, "this widespread misinterpretation is now an established part of the vernacular and there is no evident advantage in seeking to correct it."[1]

At one time, the only persons interested in Hong Kong's narcotics problems were mainly diplomats, reformers, customs officials, and the police. More recently, however, the attention of specialists in psychology and sociology has also been drawn to the Colony.

The United States in particular has turned its eyes to Hong Kong, seeking experience and know-how from those whose long contact with widespread addiction culminated, since November 1958, in several special institutions for the treatment of addicts. The oldest of them is Tai Lam Prison, an institution about which we will have more to say and which has been regarded as a model by many nations interested in treating narcotic addicts. [2] There are also two voluntary centers, one at Castle Peak, and the other on Shek Kwu Chau island and a number of organizations concerned with the care and aftercare for addicts and ex-addicts.

Hong Kong's name, moreover, has recently been drawn into the well-known American controversy over what is sometimes called the "British system" of dealing with drug addicts. Under British regulations, physicians are permitted to administer maintenance doses of narcotics to addicts within certain limited conditions and in strict accordance with professional ethics and standards. I do not want to enter into a discussion as to whether the word "system" should or should not be used to describe this British method of treatment. The controversy is not one of semantics. Rather, it concerns the *usefulness* of adopting the British approach in the United States. Opponents claim it would not work here because of our much greater number of addicts. To support this view, they point to Hong Kong as an example of a place where the "system" has not worked out satisfactorily because "the Crown Colony...... has more addicts than there are in the entire United States".[3] This controversy will again be brought up in a later part of this study.

Although a great deal has been said and a great deal written on addiction in Hong Kong, many facts about it are not yet known. We have very little data on who the Hong Kong addict is, the reason for his addiction, and how he may be treated. Hence, a study of addiction there appears desirable, especially if some of the observations can also be applied to the narcotics situation in the United States.

With the help of a grant given me most kindly by the Ford Foundation through the Research and Information Center of the National Council on Crime and Delinquency, I was able to make a brief observation tour of Hong Kong in 1961. On September 16 I left New York, and on December 3 of the same year I returned. The report submitted early in 1963 to the Ford Foundation described some of the observations I made during this trip and supplied additional data from the literature or obtained from Hong Kong authorities and other sources. Basically, that report forms our book and thus reflects, as a rule, the state of affairs towards the end of 1961. However, a second trip to Hong Kong, undertaken in fall 1963, permitted a certain number of additions and corrections, without, however, that an attempt was made to bring all data — and especially the statistical figures — up to date.

I had originally intended to limit myself to a study of treatment of narcotics addiction within Hong Kong's correctional system. Discussions preceding the trip, however, led me instead to observe as many aspects as possible of the narcotics situation. Thus, within the short time available to me, I aimed at obtaining an overall view and collected as much material as I could.

At this point I would like to express my deepest gratitude to the Ford Foundation as well as to the numerous authorities, private agencies, and persons who extended their full cooperation to me in my need for documentation.

I would also like to express my regret at not always giving full credit to those persons who furnished me with many facts and ideas. Many were civil servants whose frequently casual, on-the-spot statements could not, under local regulations, be directly quoted. In these instances, I was obliged to resort to such passive constructions as "it was reported", "it was stated", and so on, as a means of getting around the quote. For this usage, in a professional report, I must sincerely apologize to the reader.

While on my first trip to Hong Kong, I paid brief visits to the addiction treatment centers in Teheran (Iran), Singapore, Rangsit (Thailand)[4], and Macau, where I was treated most graciously. However, because of the brevity of my stay there, the differences in culture among the centers, and the language difficulties which sometimes crept into my brief visits to each, I shall not include full descriptions of these institutions in this report although I do refer to them occasionally.

The narcotics situation in Hong Kong cannot be fully understood, it seems, without two types of general data. First, the peculiar geographic, economic, and social problems of the Colony must be considered. For this reason, before getting into the question of narcotics addiction proper, I have included a brief general description of the Colony in this chapter. Secondly, the history of addiction in the Colony must also be dealt with. This history antedates the founding of Hong Kong itself, and, because narcotics were used in that part of the world (namely, China) long before Hong Kong became British in 1841, Chapter II also includes some facts on the use of opium in China.

Chapter III will deal with the present addiction situation in Hong Kong and will depict — insofar as existing figures and other data permit — the Hong Kong addict as he comes to the attention of the authorities. To my knowledge, no effort similar to this study has yet been made, with the exception, perhaps, of the limited data presented in the Hong Kong Government's *White Paper* and a few other reports. [5]

Chapters IV and V will deal with prevention and with correctional and voluntary treatment of narcotics addiction. In the final chapter, we shall review our Hong Kong observations with particular consideration of narcotics conditions in the United States. In presenting my conclusions and recommendations, may I ask the reader to keep in mind that a foreign visitor to Hong Kong is speaking, and that this visitor is hesitant to tell the Hong Kong authorities and people (who have had the narcotics problem with them for generations), on the basis of two brief visits, "what may be good for them". Therefore, I am limiting myself in the following to the comparative approach mentioned above.

Geographic and Socio-economic Characteristics of Hong Kong

In 1841, Great Britain acquired the island of Hong Kong from China as part of the spoils of the First Opium War of 1840. Through the ensuing years, Britain acquired Kowloon and the New Territories — (the latter on a 99-year lease from China beginning since 1898) (Map 1).

Of Hong Kong's 398½ square miles of land, [6] only 62 are immediately usable. [7] The remaining area has been described as "virtually useless mountainside and marshland".[8]

According to the Census of 1961, the Colony has 3 133 131 inhabitants,[9] of whom 98.17 per cent speak Chinese and only 1.21 per cent speak English as their usual language.[10] The urban areas of Hong Kong, Kowloon, and New Kowloon (the areas where most of the drug addiction is found[11]) have a population of 2 584 866,[12] or 82 per cent of the entire population. The New Territories, which comprise approximately 80 per cent of the territory, are very thinly settled and have been economically exploited on a limited scale. Only 48 per cent (1 492 887) of the inhabitants are born in Hong Kong; 46 per cent (1 425 597) come from the neighboring Chinese province of Kwangtung or from Macau — a Portuguese island 40 miles away.[13]

Economically, Hong Kong depends for the most part on her free port. Despite loss of outlets as a result of the political situation in the Far East, the port remains one of the most important ones in that area. In 1962, nearly 6 000 ocean going vessels and over 14 000 other craft entered this port.[14] In order to maintain the special nature of a free port, the authorities believe that generally little control should be imposed on trading. However, as we shall see later, this policy also makes control of narcotics smuggling very difficult.

Lately, Hong Kong's economic life has been characterized by a rapidly growing industrialization which makes good use of the skills and manpower of the refugees from the Chinese mainland and which compensates for any losses the port may have suffered. Industries of all kinds have recently sprung up — from ship dismantling and ship building to textiles, artificial flowers, and plastics. In 1960, 5 599 industrial undertakings occupied 234 533 persons in the Colony;[15] in 1961, the total working population was 1 103 444, of whom 72 per cent (793 321) were men and 28 per cent (310 123) women.[16] Wage levels varied from 3 to 7 Hong Kong dollars per day for unskilled labor,[17] to 8 to 21 for semiskilled and skilled workers.[18] We should bear these wages in mind when studying the daily amounts spent by addicts on their drug.

Legal restrictions on work hours exist only for women and young persons but not for adult men. During the fiscal year 1960—1961, 21 200

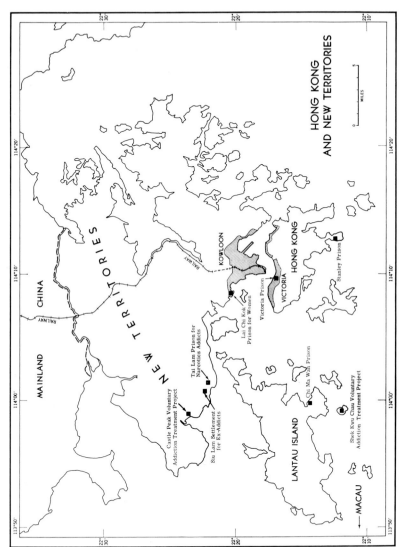

Map I

men comprising 16 per cent of the total labor force were working eight hours a day.[19] The norm is ten hours in industry,[20] but may be considerably higher in small shops. Many male workers do not enjoy a day of rest but have to work seven days a week.[21] Thus, extremely severe working conditions are frequently found, and, as we shall observe below "overwork" is indeed often cited by addicts as a cause of their addiction. Grim as this picture may look to American eyes, it must be said in all fairness that the present situation with labor regulations for women and children is a great improvement over former times.

As pointed out above, 52 per cent of the population are not born in Hong Kong. Of the 15 000 persons who are unemployed (12 311 of whom are male[22]), at least 83 per cent are foreign born.[23]

During my visit, the employment situation seemed to be somewhat irregular. With the continued growth of industry, a number of employers find it hard to recruit the type of worker they want. Although the expanding economy of the Colony is absorbing most of the skilled and many of the unskilled workers, a good deal of unemployment exists among the latter group owing to the great influx of refugees.[24] Older persons and refugees from mainland China who speak neither the Cantonese dialect nor English are the ones in particular who seem to have the greatest amount of trouble finding employment. Furthermore, owing to the high cost of transportation (as compared with the existing wage scale), Hong Kong's labor force cannot afford to be very mobile and so cannot always find employment near where they live.[25]

The Refugee Problem

A few words about the refugee problem in the Crown Colony: nearly every third person in Hong Kong is a refugee from the Chinese mainland. Of course this problem is nothing new. From time to time — especially since the 1930's — refugees from China's upheavals have flowed into Hong Kong. During my first stay, large numbers of them were coming in. Some were rejected if they were caught crossing the border, but many were successful in entering the territory and in submerging themselves within the Colony's dense population. In 1962, the world press reported that this influx had increased greatly, as had the restrictive measures by the Government. Newspaper reports I read during my second visit indicated that refugees were still illegally entering the Colony in spite of all restrictions. This influx, coupled with the natural growth of the population, has resulted in a spectacular increase in the population of Hong Kong; it is over five times that of 1945.[26] This rapid growth makes social planning most difficult and also causes a number of other severe problems.

The Housing Shortage

In addition to an extremely short supply of water, a grave housing shortage also exists. Despite the Hong Kong Government's vigorous

Illustration 1.
HONG KONG STREET SLEEPERS
Sleeping, cooking, washing clothes and bathing are done by about 29 000 persons on the Hong Kong sidewalks.

(Courtesy, Lutheran World Federation)

policy of resettlement — a policy which has benefited hundreds of thousands of persons over a number of years — a great number of squatters, roof-dwellers, street-sleepers, and others without fixed abode can still be found. A survey made in October, 1960, of certain squatter areas showed 530 000 squatters still living there, of whom 75 000 made their homes on rooftops of tenements. In addition, the number of squatters living in unsurveyed areas has been estimated at about 75 000.[28] (Ills. 1, 2 and 3).

Besides these squatter sections, the most dreadful slum quarters are also found in urban areas. With the guidance of social workers, I visited

Illustration 2.

SQUATTER AREA

Water has often to be carried into these areas which may house thousands.

(Courtesy, Lutheran World Federation)

several of them, among them the slum sections of the "Old Walled City" of Kowloon, where eight or ten persons crowded into a 5 by 8 foot cubicle without windows, cooking facilities, or sanitation. Even in the resettlement areas, the space allotted should by no means be considered by Western standards. One-room apartments, usually 120 square feet in size, housed families of four or five adults; children under ten counted as half an adult.[29]

Hong Kong is not all drudgery, unemployment, and slum. It has its luxurious areas, too. Although the figure for population density of the entire Colony is 13 persons an acre, this average is misleading since large parts of the New Territories are undeveloped. Limiting ourselves to

Illustration 3.
ROOFTOPS WITH IMPROVISED DWELLINGS
(Courtesy, Lutheran World Federation)

Hong Kong Island proper, the average is 54 persons an acre — a figure
that covers a population density that ranges from only 2 persons an
acre in the Peak district (a high-class residential area) to the unbelievable
figure of 2 819 persons an acre in a division of the Sheung Wan district.[30]

[1] White House *Ad Hoc* Panel on Drug Abuse, *Progress Report* (Washington,
  D.C., 1962), pp. 2, 13 ff.
[2] United Nations, introductory notes to "Hong Kong's Prison for Drug Addicts,"
  Bulletin on Narcotics, Vol. 13, No. 1, Jan.–March 1961, p. 13.
[3] United States Bureau of Narcotics Advisory Committee, *Comments on
  Narcotic Drugs* (Washington, U.S. Treasury Department, 1958), p. 13. See
  also p. 3.
[4] According to the *Bangkok World* of Oct. 8, 1963, pp. 1 and 14, this "sanitorium" was being abolished. As reported, the Interior Minister of Thailand
  stated that "in the five years since Thailand outlawed legal opium dens, ..
  addicts have had sufficient time to be cured. .... The time for leniency has
  passed. Addicts arrested after being cured at the sanitorium will henceforth
  be considered as lawbreakers and will be punished accordingly."
[5] Hong Kong Government, *The Problem of Narcotic Drugs in Hong Kong.
  A White Paper Laid before Legislative Council 11th November, 1959,* paras.
  8 ff. In future citations, this document will be referred to as the *1959 White
  Paper.* This and other Hong Kong Government publications referred to in
  this report are printed "By. ... (the) Government Printer at the Government
  Press", but the imprints vary slightly over the years. No effort has been made
  to render these variations in our citations.
[6] Hong Kong Government, *Hong Kong. Report for the Year 1960* (1961),
  p. 289. — In the following, this and others of these annual reports are cited
  as *Hong Kong, 1960,* or similar.
[7] Hong Kong Government, *A Problem of People* (1960), pp. 2—3.
[8] W. P. Morgan, "The Work of the Police Force in Hong Kong," *Corona*
  (British overseas Civil Service periodical), Vol. 14, No. 9, Sept. 1962,
  pp. 329—333.
[9] Hong Kong Census Commissioner (K. M. A. Barnett), *Hong Kong Report on
  the 1961 Census.* (3 Vols., 1962), Vol. 2, p. XCXX ("Final corrected figure,
  released 12-10-1961"). This publication will be referred to as the *1961 Census*
  throughout this report. By the end of 1962, the total population had grown to
  3 526 500. *Hong Kong 1962,* p. 35.
[10] *1961 Census,* Vol. 2, p. 40, Table no. 127. The figure for Chinese combines
  those for the Cantonese (79.02 %), Hakka, Hoklo, Sze Yap, and Shanghai
  "dialects", and for Kuo Yu (commonly known as "Mandarin").
[11] In Kowloon is located the "Old Walled City", formerly a no-man's land of law
  enforcement where — until 1959 — drugs could be consumed in the open
  without official intervention.
[12] *1961 Census,* Vol. 2, p. XCIX.
[13] *1961 Census,* Vol. 2, p. 33, Table 118.

14 *Illicit Traffic: Hong Kong: Statement by the Delegation of the United King-
    dom and Northern Ireland to the United Nations for the Eighteenth Session
    of the Commission on Narcotics.* (U.N. Document E/CN.7/L. 262; 1963),
    p. 2. Hereafter this publication is cited as *Illicit Traffic: Hong Kong.*
15 *Hong Kong 1960,* p. 355.
16 *1961 Census,* Vol. 2, p. 1, Table 143.
17 One Hong Kong Dollar equals approximately 17½ U.S. cents.
18 Hong Kong Department of Labour, *Annual Departmental Report* 1960/61,
    para. 97.
19 *Ibid.,* para. 102.
20 *Ibid.,* para. 103.
21 Andrew T. Roy, "Hong Kong" from *On Asia's Rim* (New York, Friendship
    Press. 1962), p. 129.
22 Vol. 3, p. 29, Table 245.
23 *Ibid.,* p. 34, Table 251.
24 Hong Kong Department of Labor, *op. cit.,* para. 222.
25 Roy, *op. cit.,* pp. 128—129.
26 In 1945, at the end of the Japanese occupation, the population comprised
    600 000 inhabitants; Hong Kong Government, *A Problem of People,* (1960),
    p. 3.
27 The daily water consumption of a Hong Kong resident was recently described
    quite aptly as "one fifth of an average American shower"; S. Boal, "Hong
    Kong: Its Many Splendored Face" in *Diners' Club Magazine,* Vol. 14, No. 8,
    October 1963, pp. 28—35, 40.
28 *Hong Kong 1960,* p. 167. Since then, these figures may have diminished
    somewhat. The *1961 Census* is not too revealing as its classification system
    groups together housing types of very different quality. (See Vol. I, Appendix
    V, Code 1, p. XXV, and Vol. 2, Tables 001 ff., pp. 1 ff.).
29 *Ibid.,* p. 165.
30 *1961 Census,* Vol. 1, Census Plan No. 1, and Vol. 2, p. 11, Tables 019, 019
    (supplementary).

CHAPTER II

A BRIEF HISTORY OF DRUG ADDICTION IN CHINA
AND HONG KONG

Although the short duration of my visits did not permit a detailed study of the history of drug abuse in the Colony, the long tradition of opium in both Hong Kong and the Chinese mainland warrant at least a brief historical account. This chapter is based mainly on data easily accessible in historical literature; only to a lesser degree were contemporary accounts and other primary sources used.

During the T'ang Dynasty (618—907 A.D.) in China, opium was already used for medicinal purposes[1] — a fact which leads us to believe that addiction to it also may not have been completely unknown in early times.

Contrary to an old belief, it was not the British who introduced the Chinese people to smoking opium; the habit may have come from Indonesia. In any case, the Portuguese imported the drug to China long before the British did.[2] Later on, however, the East India Company began shipping the drug from India, where it was grown in large quantities. By the early eighteenth century, the annual import of opium into China amounted to about two hundred "chests",[3] of about 140 to 150 pounds each, a year — a modest quantity when compared to that of later years.

The Chinese soon became apprised of the dangers of narcotics and, in 1729, an Imperial edict was issued forbidding the sale of opium and the maintenance of places where it could be smoked.[4] Despite this edict, however, the opium imports into China increased steadily. By 1800 to 1821, about 5000 chests a year were coming into the country.[5]

Other nations also participated in this trade. For example, American China traders imported Turkish opium, which was inferior to the Indian product on which the East India Company had a monopoly.[6] Business reasons, rather than ethical considerations, may have been responsible for the fact that the British played a more prominent part in the Chinese opium trade than other Western countries.

Around 1800 the Chinese Government declared the importation of opium illegal.[7] Authorities on the provincial and lower levels, however, frequently ignored this declaration. Large scale smuggling developed in which both Chinese and foreigners participated very profitably. To this day, the firms of some nineteenth century Western opium traders continue to exist. They are now highly respectable business houses along other lines.

Here, a few remarks are necessary about general trading conditions prevailing between China and the West at that time. The Chinese Government had imposed severe restrictions on all trade with the West. Since it was the Western traders who were seeking commercial relations, China was in a position to insist on such restrictions as, for example, limiting foreign merchants to only one port, Canton. Indeed, merchants were not even permitted to bring their ships to Canton itself but to Whampoa Island, thirteen miles below, where their "factories" were located. Their families were not allowed at all and usually remained at nearby Portuguese Macau. During the annual trading season, Western merchants were permitted only a limited number of visits to Canton. Their contact with the Chinese population was restricted to a minimum; all commercial dealings, and particularly contact with the Chinese authorities, had to go through a group of Chinese intermediaries called the Co-Hong merchants.[8] At the end of each season the traders had to leave China, and usually retired to Macau.

Up to the early part of the eighteenth century, the principle of equality among sovereign states, which today is the very basis of intercourse among nations both large and small, was not yet generally put into practice. Large, powerful states considered their legal status superior to that of the smaller, less mighty nations — even where questions of mere diplomatic protocol were concerned. At the end of the century, the principle of equality was generally recognized in the West. Not so in China. The "Middle Kingdom" continued to insist on the old principle of inequality in its dealings with the countries of the "Outer Barbarians" until finally it was forced to give it up, after losing its battles against Great Britain.

The Chinese Imperium considered itself the center of the universe, to which all other nations had to pay homage. When the Western nations sent emissaries to China on diplomatic missions, they had no chance of negotiating on an equal basis. Thus, as late as 1838—1839, the Chinese Anti-Opium Commissioner Lin Tse-Hsu, himself only a government official, wrote to Queen Victoria admonishing her about the British opium trade and treating her as though she was merely a tributary to the Celestial Kingdom. [9]

Although this attitude was, of course, unrealistic, it nevertheless expresses the Chinese Government's distrust of Westerners — a distrust that becomes understandable in the light of the fact that trade with Westerners was limited primarily to dealings with sailors, traders, and adventurers.

As a rule, the forbidden opium trade did not go through the port of Canton, but through LinTin Island, situated at the mouth of the Pearl River not far from Hong Kong and Macau. Here, fast and well-armed foreign clipper ships unloaded the opium into storage hulks called "receiving ships". From LinTin Island, "centipedes" and "scrambling dragons" — fast Chinese craft — took the opium to spots hidden along the Chinese coast.

The situation, as it existed, caused a great number of problems and stirred up a good deal of resentment on both sides. The Chinese — understandably — felt that foreigners coming to their country should respect their laws. Economically, the ever growing opium import had reversed the stream of silver which originally had flown into China from its exports of tea, rhubarb and other goods. Chinese statesmen considered this outflow of Chinese silver as disastrous, especially since it was accompanied by a devaluation of Chinese copper coin, the "cash". [10] The foreign merchants needed cargo when sailing towards China to make their trips worthwhile, and there was nothing as suitable as opium which they could sell easily on the Chinese market. Furthermore, Great Britain needed an outlet for her Indian opium production which provided in 1850, for example, one-fifth of India's revenue. [11] The cessation of the opium export to China would indeed have been disastrous to India's finances.[12]

The Westerners, on the other hand, resented the humiliations and abuses to which they were continuously subjected by the Co-Hong merchants and by a corrupted Chinese bureaucracy. Above all, the Western nations became unwilling to be treated as inferior tributaries from the outer realm of the Middle Kingdom and felt they should be recognized as equal partners in international negotiations.

The opium struggle of the nineteenth century has often been explained only in terms of the commercial interests involved, but, as mentioned, less rational reasons for the struggle were also present. For both, opium had also become the focus of a struggle for prestige: China asserted her sovereignty and power by requesting suppression of the drug traffic, and the British, unfortunately, chose as a means of protest against the treatment they received the insistence on trading in opium.

In retrospect, the West's insistence on importing this damaging drug to China against her will does seem wholly unscrupulous, but when looked at in the proper perspective of its own time, it becomes apparent that the West was not always fully aware of its dangers. Indeed, in the eighteenth and early nineteenth centuries Europeans often held quite idealized notions about opium. Opium was often taken as a medicine "for just about everything" in the West — especially orally as *laudanum*.[13] In 1700, a London physician described the opium experience as follows: "it is indeed so unexpressibly fine and sweet a *Pleasure,* that it is very difficult for me to describe, or any to concede it, but such as actually feel it; for 't is as if a *Good Genius* possessed, or informed a Man; therefore, People do commonly call it a *heavenly Condition,* as if no worldly *Pleasure* was to be compar'd with it......"[14]

During the Romantic Age around 1800 people had become particularly interested in the dreams that opium supposedly caused. The writer Thomas de Quincey, himself an addict and critical of the drug, elaborated on the mystery they revealed to him; the composer Hector Berlioz set them a musical monument to opium dreams in his *Symphonie Fantastique.*

The dangers of the drug, to be sure, were recognized to some extent. As early as 1788, for example, Warren Hastings spoke of opium as "a pernicious article of luxury",[15] but opponents of its use were not really in the majority. Rather, like today's teetotalers and non-smokers, they were the exceptions rather than the rule. Or, as the opium trader Matheson put it, they were the "Saints".[16]

Up until our time, opposition to narcotics was frequently considered "the attitude of a few". Thus, a statement made in 1922 by Owen Rutter, president of the British North Borneo Company, in which that Company's successful operation of the opium business was described, concluded: "Apart from the point of view of persons interested in stamping out opium smoking there is not very much to be said against the Company's trade in the drug."[17]

Another reason for the West's easy dismissal of the Far Eastern drug problem was the often-held belief that, regardless of its effects on Europeans, "there is something about the Chinese physique and character that seems to make the use of opium not only relatively harmless but even necessary to his happiness and well-being."[18] The belief, considered by Asians to be characteristic of Western feelings of superiority, was responsible for many of their embittered feelings toward the West.[19]

The West has often considered China's accusation of having corrupted its people through opium as hypocritical by pointing out the fact that a large number of Chinese themselves profited from opium, and especially through the cultivation of the poppy in China itself. Indeed not all of the opium consumed was imported. The Chinese themselves grew poppies; the growing of poppies was already spread in the early 1800's[20] and the Chinese expanded it considerably further in the course of time.

A certain justification can, however, be found for this. Since China could not stop the importation of the drug from abroad as a result of conditions imposed by the treaties which she had been obliged to sign after her defeat in the two Opium Wars, curtailing poppy cultivation would hardly have reduced the smoking of the drug. The smaller production within the country would have been immediately compensated by larger imports and, thus, the country's finances would have been drained even further.

Let us go back to early-nineteenth century China. Tension mounted. In 1834, British merchants in Canton requested that the British Government back up their negotiations for better trading conditions with force. Around this time, too, they suggested that the British authorities seek to occupy Hong Kong.

In 1838—1839, the quantity of opium imported amounted to 40 000 chests. It was at this stage that the events occurred which led to the first "Opium War". One of the most important incidents was the seizure of over 20 000 chests of opium from foreign merchants in Canton under the direction of Lin Tse-Hsu, the Imperial Commissioner for the Suppression of the Opium Trade. As a war indemnity, the Chinese were obliged to pay $ 21 000 000 (including $ 6 000 000 for the opium seized), and to surrender the island of Hong Kong to the British.[21] The occupation took place in 1841; the Treaty of Nanking of 1842 confirmed Great Britain's possession of Hong Kong.

British Occupation of Hong Kong

In the beginning, the British were not always happy about the new acquisition. Hong Kong, termed a "barren island" by Lord Henry Palmerston, British Foreign Secretary,[22] had only a few small villages and a population of approximately 7 500 inhabitants.[23]

Already in 1841, Hong Kong's real development began. By December of that year, "workers attracted by the employment available" had helped swell the population to 12 000;[24] by 1844, the port of Hong Kong was handling 538 ships.[25]

After signing the peace treaty with China in 1842 the British officially condemned opium smuggling. Sir Henry Pottinger, Administrator and first Governor of Hong Kong from 1841 to 1844, issued a proclamation threatening confiscation of the cargo of any British ship found carrying opium. Despite this proclamation, however, the illegal trade was not hindered, a fact which led James Matheson, of the leading British trading firm of Jardine and Matheson, to write in 1843: "Sir Henry never means to act upon it (the proclamation) and no doubt privately considers it a good joke. At any rate he allows the drug to be landed and stored at Hong Kong."[26]

Thus, from the very beginning, opium played an important role in the Colony; indeed it had been one of the most important reasons for making Hong Kong British.

Previously, British insurance companies did not cover opium stored in the "receiving ships", floating makeshift storehouses situated in such open anchorages as Lintin Island. At that time, the owners themselves had to bear most or all of the risks involved.

Now the drug could be stored, properly insured, in a port under British sovereignty; and instead of using hulks, solid warehouses could be built.[27] In 1844, Sir John F. Davis, then new Governor of Hong Kong, stated that "almost every person possessed of capital who is not connected with government employment is employed in the opium trade". By 1845, eighty clipper ships operated in the opium trade from Hong Kong; of these, thirty-two were owned by the two firms of Jardine & Matheson and Dent & Co.[28] In 1846, 9 348 chests of opium were imported to Hong Kong.[29]

From 1845—1849, over 40 000 chests worth $ 16 000 000 were stored in Hong Kong. At that time, too, the port was handling at least three-fourths or more of the entire Indian crop of opium.[30]

Despite the improved conditions in the opium trade, it still had its difficulties as evidences in the following letter written by James Matheson:

> "The Gazelle was unnecessarily detained at Hong Kong in consequence of Captain Crocker's repugnance to receiving opium on the Sabbath. We have every respect for persons entertaining strict religious principles, but we fear that very godly people are not suited for the drug trade. Perhaps it would be better that the Captain should resign."[31]

Between 1841 and 1843, nine men died in Hong Kong's prison. Of these, some apparently were opium smokers whose deaths occurred during their withdrawal.[32]

Around 1845, an "opium farm", a monopoly, was established by the Government, not without opposition from the big opium merchants who feared for their control of the drug market.[33]

The Reverend George Smith (later to become the first Anglican Bishop of Victoria, Hong Kong), who visited the Colony in May, 1846, described the activities of Mr. A-quey, the "farmer". While all the Chinese in Hong Kong belonged to the lowest socio-economic stratum at that time, he wrote, A-quey was "the only wealthy Chinese on the island" and "by the rights which he has acquired as the purchaser of the opium farm, wields an instrument of oppressive exaction over the rest of the Chinese settlers. At one period he was in the habit of visiting the native boats and private houses, in order to seize every hulk of opium suspected of being sold without his license. Accompanied for that purpose by native or by Indian police, he exercised an inquisitorial power for enforcing his monopoly over the timid Chinese..."[34]

Incidentally, the Reverend Smith also undertook, by means of interviews, the beginnings of a systematic investigation into the physical and psycho-social conditions of drug addicts. In the Chinese city of Amoy Smith visited ten opium houses "in order that I might possess ten consecutive cases of opium smokers, and gain positive testimony from their own confessions on the subject. We generally took the first man in each house whom we beheld in the act of inhaling the fumes..." The descriptions of these ten cases were reported in Smith's book.[35]

In 1848, opium imports had risen to 45 479 chests,[36] or about five times the 1845 amount. By 1850, the imports climbed still further to 52 000 chests.

In 1858, the opium monopoly, which had been discontinued for ten years as of 1848, was again farmed out at the price of £ 4 508/6/8. At this time a scandal broke out among the people of Hong Kong. They, along with the local press, became enraged — not by the idea of a monopoly on opium or the abuses of this monopoly — but by the fact that Chun Tai Kung, the new monopolist, had obtained this privilege through the machinations of his legal counsel, who held also the post of a Colonial Secretary in Hong Kong. The result of the scandal was an official investigation, which led to the conclusion that the Colonial Secretary had not behaved dishonestly; he had merely exercised poor judgment.[37]

In the same year the Treaty of Tientsin was signed in the Second Opium War, legalizing the importation of opium into China.[38]

However, smugglers continued to flourish, in an effort to bypass the Chinese import duty and tax on transit to the interior — in the words of the British Minister to Peking in 1868, Hong Kong remained "an immense smuggling depot".[39]

Indeed, the smuggling of opium was described in 1870 by William H. Seward, who had been Abraham Lincoln's Secretary of State during the Civil War years and who was then taking a world trip.[40] He and his party, traveling from Hong Kong to Canton on December 28 on the steamer Kin-San, reported:

> "From the deck, we noticed a native trader, who at intervals advanced to the bulwark, and threw into the water small bundles of hay and straw. We observed that, in every case, natives rowed from the shore in small boats, and picked up this refuse. Our friends, who knew the trick, informed us that the bundles of hay and straw contained packages of opium. Another trader dropped a sealed bottle into the river. A partner, who was waiting on the bank, took it up and found in it the prices current of opium in London. Smuggling wears only this thin covering in China." [41]

The extensive smuggling led to a "customs blockade" by the Chinese authorities, who harassed smugglers by means of launches and customs stations set up in the immediate vicinity of the Colony. The smugglers responded by stronger means. In 1877, Governor J. Pope Hennessy quoted to the Earl of Carnarvon a statement by the Acting Captain Superintendent of Police in Hong Kong:

> "Mr. Creagh says that the smuggling from Hong Kong to the mainland of China of salt and opium, is carried on in vessels constructed and equipped expressly for running the blockade of Chinese Revenue Cruisers. The smuggling Junks are well armed, and sometimes offer a desperate resistance to the Chinese Government vessels. He mentions a case that occurred in November last, in which three or four of these smuggling Junks, after exchanging fire with the Chinese Government Steamer *Peng-Chow-hoi,* sought refuge in Hong Kong Harbour, where they were refitted. He mentions that the construction and equipment of such vessels render them better suited for piratical operations than for legitimate trade, and that the class of men trained up in them cannot be expected to show much respect for the law of any country." [42]

Governor Hennessy strongly felt that smuggling into China from Hong Kong should be discouraged — last but not least because of its close connection to piracy. In several dispatches to the Colonial Secretary in London, he promised to take steps, and the Earl of Carnarvon backed him up. [42]

The Colony was also doing business with the United States then, sending her not only large numbers of Chinese emigrants (mainly from the vicinity of Canton) but also opium; an estimated 3 000 chests of opium were shipped each year to California through the port of Hong Kong.[43] Of the Chinese emigrants who had come to America, many returned to the homeland; so that when Seward was traveling to the Far East on the Pacific Mail Liner, *China,* also 500 Chinese passengers were on board, traveling in the "steerage". A dark room of canvas was constructed for them so that they could smoke opium.[44]

While in Canton, Seward's party described a visit they paid to an opium den. They were taken

> "through a dark passage to a suite of small rooms, faintly lighted from the roof. The seclusion, darkness, and silence of the place indicated that something furtive was going on there. On either side of a long chamber was a dais divided into sections, in each section two men reclining *vis-a-vis* — between them a miniature table six inches high. Before each of the smokers, on the table, rested a pipe, a tiny opium-pot, and a burning lamp. Here, as in the teahouse, there is no respect of rank or wealth. The poor and the rich lie down together. Each assists the other in the delicate task of lighting the opium and filling the bowl of the pipe. We spoke to two or three of the smokers, who were only at the beginning of the siesta, and received from them respectful and gentle answers. We tried in vain to rouse others to consciousness, who were in the stage of blissful revery, although their eyes were open, and they were sadly smiling. When the smoker recovers from the inebriation, if he has sufficient strength he repairs home; otherwise, he is removed to another apartment, and remains there perhaps twenty-four hours, recovering strength to depart. Was it an imagination of ours that the keeper of this hell wore a base and sinister look as he stood behind his counter in a dark closet, surrounded by packages of the pernicious drug, which he weighed out to his customers a pennyweight of opium against a pennyweight of silver?"[45] (Ill. 4.)

Opposition to the Opium Trade

As we have seen, the Chinese had prohibited the import and use of opium for smoking. But during the nineteenth century, the continuous pressure by the Western powers — Great Britain, in particular — greatly enhanced the spread of the habit in China. In the course of time, the Chinese, quite understandably, were to place the blame for the opium abuse in their country squarely on the shoulders of the Western powers. In fact, as early as the 1840's, when the Reverend George Smith revealed to addicts in Amoy that he was an English missionary, "they exposed the inconsistency of my rebuking their habit of smoking opium, while my countrymen brought them the means of indulging it." [46]

But opposition to opium was beginning to shape-up in the West. In

Illustration 4.
OPIUM SMOKERS IN CANTON, C. 1873
(From *William S. Seward's Travels around the World*. 1873).

March, 1840, an opium debate took place in the British House of Commons, in which the young Gladstone rose up against the "infamous and atrocious traffic" in opium.[47] Abolitionist feelings started to be taken into account by British officials. Thus, as has already been described, the British Plenipotentiary in Hong Kong, Sir Henry Pottinger issued a proclamation against the smuggling of opium in the early 1840's, a proclamation never intended to be implemented and issued merely as a gesture to please the abolitionists in England, the "Saints" as Matheson called them.[48]

In 1874, the Anglo-Oriental Society for the Suppression of the Opium Trade was formed in England; and in Hong Kong, a commission was also formed for the purpose of enquiring into the operations of the opium monopoly.[49] In the 1880's, the first legal restrictions were promulgated.[50]

Together with provisions against gambling, the legal restrictions against opium led to an increase of admissions to the Colony's correctional facilities. They were mostly short-term prisoners whose number rose from 3 444 in 1890 to 5 231 in 1891, i.e. an increase of over 50 per cent. The Colonial Surgeon, Dr. B. D. Ayres was sceptical about the possibility of eradicating opium smoking from the Chinese population "by law" and comments:

> "Yet opium-smoking does not do 1 000th part of the harm to either the individual or his family that alcohol does at home."[51]

Nor is it as injurious, in his opinion, as tobacco smoking.[52] Dr. Ayres' report describes an experiment whereby the surgeon had smoked a large quantity of opium himself under observation, and "had felt no effects from the smoking whatever." Having been placed in charge of Victoria Gaol eighteen years earlier, he reports that, after his first three months, he had eliminated the then customary "extra diet" for addicts, consisting of a Laudanum mixture, quinine pills and gin. Having examined over a thousand addicted prisoners in the course of the time, he had "not been able to find that the habit affected them in any way physically or mentally."[53]

Nevertheless in 1891, a vote in the House of Commons condemned the opium trade and a Royal Commission of Enquiry was set up.[54] In

Hong Kong an anti-opium campaign, seeking to abolish the opium farm so as to gain better control of the drug took place. The farmer was now limited to a maximum production of 1 800 chests a year. Trade declined; imports fell from 67 429 chests in 1889 to 34 292, or almost half of that, by 1898. The proceeds of the opium farm diminished from $ 447 600 in 1890 to $ 357 666 in 1898.[55]

The farmer (in 1895 the *Wan Foo* or "Thousand Blessings" Company) had, as he had already in the early 1840's, the right of search. Because of these searches, executed by personnel that was not always of the highest integrity, the monopolist was always very unpopular with the Chinese population of Hong Kong. The regulations of the Wan Foo Company of December 12, 1895 may be reproduced here in English translation:

1. Visiting businessmen arriving in Hong Kong from other ports by steamship, are exempted if found to carry opium of only a few cents worth.

2. All visiting businessmen arriving in Hong Kong for residence or for transit are free to carry opium for personal use. However, they must notify this Company in advance for a license. For every ounce carried there is a due of 0.40 cents.

3. In searching for smuggled opium, each inspector will make a bodily search. The Company is compelled to carry out such a practice because it frequently encounters fraudulent persons who hide opium on their bodies in order to evade the tax. In case of prominent Hong Kong personalities who fear loss of face, they may apply at this Company for a pass of immunity from search. However, the applicant must supply a photograph to be attached to this document in order to avoid mistakes on the part of the inspectors and also because, in case of loss, the pass may fall into the hands of dishonest persons who may use it for smuggling purposes.

4. If any inspector is found to have planted evidence for the purpose of a frame-up, the complainant may report it to this Company. If ascertained to be true, the inspector in question will be dismissed without leniency and the complainant may file charges against him with the proper authorities. This Company will not whitewash him.

5. The owner of confiscated opium smoking equipment may apply at this Company for the redemption at a fair price.

6. Pursuant to the laws of Hong Kong, anyone who is found with over 2 oz. of opium — regardless of whether the opium he possesses be provided by this Company or by himself — will be criminally prosecuted. This regulation has

been in effect for a considerable period of time and was not originated by this Company. In view, however, of the many persons who, inadvertently, violate this regulation, we hereby wish to bring it to the particular attention of everybody concerned for his guidance.

> This twelfth day of the
> twelfth month of the
> twentieth year of the
> Emperor Kuang Hsu.

> The Wan Foo Company [56]

At the turn of the century when the Boxer Rebellion caused a rise in nationalism, anti-opium sentiments gained further momentum among Chinese reformers. In the Colony itself, however, the opium trade still remained important to Hong Kong's economy. In 1906, for example, this trade in opium amounted to over £ 5 000 000, over £ 2 000 000 of which the government took in revenue. [57] In China, too, the opium revenue was a financial pillar of public administration. To illustrate, in 1905, when the Hong Kong Government gave a loan to the Viceroy of Hupeh and Hunan Provinces for the construction of the Canton-Hankow railway, the opium revenue of the two provinces served as security for the loan. [58]

Around 1908 public pressure in England had grown strong enough to obtain measures for reducing India's opium export. This, in turn, led to discussions on the topic of the drug in the Colony of Hong Kong. [59] There were then 190 divans (as opium dens are called in Hong Kong) consisting of a "single room which, if quite full, might accommodate 30 persons at a time", but were occupied in general with only 13 or 14. They kept open from 6 a.m. to midnight, and were supervised by the Police and Sanitary Department and the Protector of the Chinese. [60] The Governor, Sir Frederick Lugard visited them personally. Although his opinion of the divans was quite favorable — he found them "quiet and orderly", and in that respect contrasting to the English "pubs" [61] — the government, nevertheless, ordered divans to close by March 1, 1909. On that day, twenty-six divans were actually shut down. [62] Import and export of opium were curtailed.

The Opium Farm at the time of Governor Lugard's report was in the hands of Singapore merchants. The farm was as much disliked as ever because of their offensive practices of searching but, as Sir Frederick remarks, "the odium would be incurred by the Government if the Farm were abolished."[63]

In 1910, the opium farm was leased for three years — for the last time. The government obtained only $ 1 830 200 annually for the monopoly — 11 per cent less than the last time[64] — and Great Britain had to grant the Colony a subsidy to replace the loss of opium revenue.[65]

In 1913—14, the Colony set up its own monopoly, and at the same time reduced the amount of the drug sales.[66]

In 1912, Great Britain was one of the signers of the international *Convention for the Suppression of the Abuse of Opium and Other Drugs* (The Hague, Netherlands). Because of the onset of World War I, however, it was not until 1924 that a committee was actually formed in Hong Kong to study implementation of the Convention and to make recommendations.[67] In the course of making suggestions on specific points in the document, the committee, on the whole, came to the conclusion that as long as the neighboring provinces in China permitted more or less unlimited consumption of opium, Hong Kong could not expect to be completely successful in her fight against it. Ironically enough, at approximately the same time, a representative of the Chinese National Anti-Opium Association, who attended the Opium Conference in Geneva, Switzerland, argued that China could never be successful in fighting against opium if its use was legal in neighboring Hong Kong and Macau.[68]

The observations of the Hong Kong Committee throw some light on the narcotics situation then prevailing in the Colony. Like other observers, the Committee had numerous difficulties with existing statistics. It had to base its own population estimates on the amount of "nightsoil" (fecal matter) produced by the population.[69] The committee estimated that approximately 20 to 25 per cent of the adult Chinese population (including 1 per cent to 2 per cent of the females) used opium, and that these percentages had increased slightly during the previous six or seven years. As to the Chinese of the "better classes", they were, according to the Committee Report, "inclined to regard the opium habit as discreditable, much as they would regard betting as discreditable, but they are certainly not prepared to practice what they may possibly preach. Public opinion might not countenance too open a parade of either gambling or opium smoking, but at least it has no great fault to find with the not too ostentatious practice of the latter habit. Opium smoking in China has perhaps the same popular support as betting has in England, and the one practice is probably as difficult to eradicate as the other."[70]

The Chinese population did not cooperate too well with the Hong Kong Government. They objected to the search methods then used by the authorities. Public opinion was "not emphatic against smugglers", who could frequently "outbid" the government.[71]

The committee did not recommend an increase in penalties for drug offenses because the existing penalties were already "of exceptional severity" and as effective as they could possibly be under the circumstances.[72] The report noted that, in addition to the usual smoking of opium, the swallowing of opium — a method of consumption used mainly in India — was also spreading in the Colony.[73]

According to the committee's estimate, about half the opium consumed in Hong Kong was legal, the other half illegal.[74] The government opium was of higher quality and more expensive; the illegal opium, which was available in unlimited quantities, was not so good, but cheaper: "The only persons who need purchase government opium are those who want a high grade product and those who prefer to pay a high price rather than risk the penalty for the use of smuggled opium".[75] In discussing whether the government should raise or lower its price, the committee recommended that no change in price be made, since a higher price would increase the consumption of illegal opium while a lower price would raise the consumption of *legal* opium, which the government wanted to limit.[76] Further, an immediate and complete prohibition would create a situation which, in view of its unlimited availability in China, "would get entirely out of hand."[77]

The committee also mentioned that the Colony received a "considerable revenue" from narcotics but it (the committee) had "ignored the financial aspect of the opium question".[78] Interesting in this connection is the fact that, according to a statement made in 1924 in the British Parliament, the opium revenue in Hong Kong comprised almost 22.4 per cent of the total revenue of the Colony.[79]

Registration of addicts, as suggested by the Advisory Committee of the League of Nations, was rejected by the Hong Kong Committee as impractical due to the fluctuating population of the Colony.[80]

A report in 1930 listed the revenue at only 7.23 per cent of the Colony's total revenue,[81] and the Colony was still "flooded with illicit opium".[82] This report also noted the relatively frequent appearance of heroin in pill form, which was being manufactured in nearby Macau.[83] Two years later, in 1932, the governmental revenue from opium decreased still further to 5.1 per cent of the total revenue.[84] Also mentioned in the report was the trafficker's use of women and children for smuggling purposes.[85]

Toward the end of the 1930's, when Wood's *Brief History* was[86] written, the Government was still receiving revenue from opium and, doubtless, continued to do so until 1941, when Hong Kong was occupied by the Japanese during World War II.

Information on the handling of the drug question by the Japanese occupation forces of Hong Kong is not readily available and one has to rely a good deal on oral testimony.

As it appears, the Japanese occupation forces, as one of their very first measures after arrival, banned opium. This order, however, was mostly a propaganda matter in order to demonstrate to the Chinese population that the Japanese would not, unlike the British, poison their Asian brothers through opium. Later the picture changed and opium was admitted again. Smokers were registered; opium in sufficient quantities was sold to the addicts and divans were permitted.[87] It seems the benefits of the business were deliberately directed towards collaborators and informers among the Hong Kong population who received as a reward for their help, the authority for distribution of the drug in their local quarters. Conceivably, the tranquilizing effect of opium might help a power engaged in warfare to keep the population of an occupied enemy territory from active resistance.[88]

As for the Allied powers, they held several meetings beginning January 1943 at the request of the United States on the drug problems they would have to face in the Far East after reoccupying the lost territories. At these meetings it was emphasized:

"that if the American Navy were to capture Hong Kong, for

instance, under the status quo the official opium stores would probably be reopened immediately; that the American Navy could not indirectly license the opium trade abroad when it is condemned at home. The belief was expressed that one way of making sure that the narcotic traffic is controlled is to increase the penalties; unfortunately, in the areas in the Far East where the opium monopolies exist the penalties are low".[89]

On November 10, 1943, the British Government, after having received an *aide-memoire* from the United States, announced its intention to abolish the legalized sale of opium in its Far Eastern territories.[90]

When the British, in 1946, reassumed authority in Hong Kong, their opium policy became abolitionist. The Government opium monopoly was not renewed and all consumption of dangerous drugs, except for legitimate medical purposes, was forbidden.[91]

Since then, the past is almost the present, and, in the following chapters, the reader will find a description of some of the historical events concerning narcotics that took place after World War II. As already pointed out, Hong Kong's population of 600 000 at the end of the Japanese occupation exploded to over 3 500 000 in 1962 — an increase due primarily to the influx of refugees from the Chinese mainland which had become communist by 1949.

Among these refugees came also many addicts and traffickers to Hong Kong. It is claimed that émigré gangsters (especially from Shanghai) contributed to the change from opium to heroin consumption in Hong Kong during the 1950's.[92]

Hindering the Hong Kong Government in its measures against narcotics was the fact that British sovereignity was not exercised over the Old Walled City of Kowloon for many years because of a doubtful legal situation. The Walled City was built from 1843 to 1847, when Kowloon was still Chinese. Under the Peking Convention of 1898, the Chinese Government had reserved the continuance of the jurisdiction of Chinese officials in the district. It appears, though, as if this jurisdiction had already ceased to be exercised one year later. A good deal of it was demolished by the Japanese during the war.[93] What remains is bare of any romantic connotations that the name "Walled City" may suggest.

It consists of abominable slum streets, too narrow for vehicles to drive through. Habitations there are overcrowded to the extreme, airless, and lack the most elementary sanitation facilities. Until 1959, the Walled City remained virtually a no-man's land of lawlessness. People in Hong Kong remember how opium divans and other places of vice had flourished in the open at that time. On November 30, 1959, however, the Hong Kong Full Court ruled that the Courts of the Colony had jurisdiction over the Walled City and the district was cleaned up then.[94]

A social worker who had worked in the Walled City many years, guided me through the district. He informed me that formerly he had always emptied his pockets before entering the district for fear that addicts there would pickpocket his watch, fountain pen, or other valuables.

Only when the courts had decided that the Government could policy this territory was the area cleaned up and the law enforced. Henceforth, the Hong Kong Government was in a much better position to take anti-narcotic measures. In November, 1959, it began a large-scale drive, establishing the Secretary of Chinese Affairs as the Government agency responsible for the coordination of all services and organizations involved.

[1] G. B. Endacott, *A History of Hong Kong* (London, Oxford University Press, 1958), p. 10.

[2] M. Collis, *Foreign Mud. Being an Account of the Opium Imbroglio at Canton in the 1830's and the Anglo-Chinese War that Followed* (New York, Alfred A. Knopf, 1947), p. 63.

[3] Endacott, *op. cit.*, p. 10.

[4] J. P. Gavit, *Opium* (New York, Brentano's, 1927), p. 122.

[5] Endacott, *op. cit.*, p. 10.

[6] Maurice Collis, *op. cit.*, p. 63.

[7] Endacott, *op. cit.*, p. 10.

[8] Collis, *op. cit.*, pp. 13—91.

[9] Collis, *op. cit.*, pp. 220—225.

[10] A. Waley, *The Opium War through Chinese Eyes* (London, Allen & Unwin, 1958), p. 25.

[11] Collis, *op cit.*, p. 297.

[12] Waley, *op. cit.*, p. 31.

[13] D. Ebin (Ed.), The Drug Experience: *First-Person Accounts of Addicts, Writers, Scientists and Others* (New York, Orion Press, 1961), p. 117.

[14] *Ibid.*, p. 118. Quoted by Ebin from *The Mysteries of Opium Reveal'd*, by John Jones (London, R. Smith, 1701).

15 Cited by Gavit, *op. cit.*, p. 11.

16 Collis, *op. cit.*, p. 297.

17 Cited by Gavit, *op. cit.*, p. 57.

18 *Ibid.*, p. 121. (This passage does not represent Gavit's own views; rather, it is his commentary on the prevailing attitude).

19 *Ibid.* p. 55.

20 Waley, *op. cit.* p. 26.

21 Gavit, *Opium,* p. 123. Gavit claims that actually the opium was worth only one-third of this amount.

22 Collis, *op. cit.*, pp. 300—301; see also Endacott, *op. cit.*, p. 18.

23 George Smith, *A Narrative of the Exploratory Visit to Each of the Consular Cities of China, and to the Islands of Hong Kong and Chusan* (New York, Harper and Brothers, 1847), p. 450.

24 Endacott, *op. cit.*, p. 32.

25 *Ibid.*, p. 74.

26 Quoted by Collis, *op. cit.*, p. 297.

27 Endacott, *op. cit.*, p. 74. The firm of Jardine & Matheson soon built a granite "go-down", a storehouse, and used in addition, an exceptionally large hulk. (See Collis, *op. cit.*, p. 297).

28 Endacott, *op. cit.*, p. 73.

29 *Ibid.*, p. 75.

30 *Ibid.*, p. 30.

31 Cited in Collis, *op. cit.*, p. 281.

32 James Wm. Norton-Kyshe, *The History of the Laws and Courts of Hong Kong* (London, T. Fisher Unwin, 1898), Vol. 1, pp. 30—32.

33 Endacott, *op. cit.*, p. 73.

34 G. Smith, *op. cit.*, p. 452.

35 G. Smith, *op. cit.*, "Facts Illustrative of Prevalence and Effects of Opium-Smoking" Chapter 29, pp. 380—389.

36 Endacott, *op. cit.*, p. 130.

37 Norton-Kyshe, *op. cit.*, Vol. 1, p. 583.

38 Endacott, *op. cit.*, pp. 100, 189.

39 Cited *ibid.*, p. 189.

40 Dexter Perkins, "William Henry Seward" in *Dictionary of American Biography* (New York, Charles Scribner's Sons, 1935), Vol. 16, pp. 615—621.

41 *William H. Seward's Travels around the World.* Olive R. Seward, ed., (New York, D. Appleton & Co., 1873), pp. 253—254. (Cited as *Seward's Travels* in the following).

42 Despatches between Governor J. Pope Hennessy and the Earl of Carnarvon, Principal Secretary of State for the Colonies, Nos. 32, 39, 45 and 122, of June 30, 1877, in the *Hong Kong Gazette,* June 11, 1881, pp. 455—458.

43 Endacott, *op. cit.*, p. 189.

44 *Seward's Travels,* p. 32.

45 *Ibid.*, pp. 267—269.

46 Smith, *op. cit.*, p. 382.

47 Cited by Collis, *op. cit.*, p. 269.

48 *Ibid.*, pp. 296—297.

49 Winifred A. Wood, *A Brief History of Hong Kong* (Hong Kong, South China Morning Post, c. 1940) p. 98.

50 *1959 White Paper,* para. 26.

51 Hong Kong Colonial Surgeon "Report for 1891", in: *Papers Laid before the Legislative Council of Hong Kong, 1892* No. 30/92 (Hong Kong, 1892) pp. 391—452. This publication is hereafter quoted as *Sessional Papers.*

52 *Ibid.* p. 395.

53 *Ibid.* The report contains also data about an experiment, undertaken in 1881 by the Hong Kong Government Analyst, Hugh McCallum demonstrating experts and smokers of old standing could not distinguish between opium of different morphine content and with all morphine abstracted; see Appendix, pp. 399—400.

54 The Colonial Surgeon of Hong Kong, Dr. Phineas Ayres, considered opium as harmless and wrote an extensive report in its defense in 1891. See Wood, *op. cit.,* pp. 157—160.

55 Endacott, *op. cit.,* p. 257.

56 "Hsiang-K'ang Ya-pien hui-i lu (Reminiscences on Opium in Hong Kong)", in *Hsiang-K'ang Chih-nan* (Hong Kong, Far East News Agency 1948), pp. 18—19.

57 Endacott, *op. cit.,* p. 274.

58 *Ibid.,* pp. 272—273.

59 *1959 White Paper,* para. 26: "Since about 1910, the object (of legislative control) has been to suppress opium addiction altogether."

60 Hong Kong Governor "Memorandum Regarding the Restriction of Opium in Hong Kong and China" in *Sessional Papers* (Hong Kong, 1909), No. 3/1909, pp. 25—40.

61 *Ibid.,* p. 33.

62 Endacott, *op. cit.,* p. 274.

63 Hong Kong, Governor, *op. cit.,* p. 30.

64 Endacott, *op. cit.,* p. 274.

65 Gavit, *Opium,* p. 52, quoting W. T. Gunn.

66 Endacott, *op. cit.,* p. 274.

67 Committee to Consider the Colony's Position with Regard to the Obligations Incurred under the International Opium Convention, 1912, *Report* (1924). (Cited in the following as *1924 Committee Report).*

68 Gavit, *op. cit.,* p. 166.

69 *1924 Committee Report,* section 11.

70 *Ibid.,* sec. 3.

71 *Ibid.,* sec. 6.

72 *Ibid.*

73 *Ibid.,* sec. 14.

74 *Ibid.,* sec. 5.

75 *Ibid.,* sec. 12.

76 *Ibid.,* sec. 5.

77 *Ibid.,* sec. 13.

78 *Ibid.,* sec. 2.

79 Gavit, *Opium,* p. 53.

[80] *1924 Committee Report,* sec. 9.
[81] Hong Kong Government, *Report for the Calendar Year 1930 on the Traffic in Opium and Dangerous Drugs* (c. 1931), p. 2.
[82] *Ibid.,* p. 2.
[83] *Ibid.,* p. 4. No. (12).
[84] Hong Kong Government, *Report for the Calendar Year 1932 on the Traffic in Opium and Dangerous Drugs* (c. 1933), p. 3.
[85] *Ibid.*
[86] *Op. cit.,* p. 258.
[87] This description is based on oral accounts by eye witnesses given to the author.
[88] Also on mainland China, the Japanese occupation forces had opened some new opium shops. See Randall Gould, *China in the Sun* (New York, Doubleday, 1946), p. 291.
[89] United States Treasury Department. Bureau of Narcotics. *Traffic in Opium and Other Dangerous Drugs for the Year Ended December 31, 1943: Report* (Washington, D.C., 1944), p. 3.
[90] *Ibid.*
[91] Endacott, *op. cit.,* p. 303 — see also U.S. Bureau of Narcotics, *op. cit.,* pp. 150—151.
[92] See *1959 White Paper,* para. 18.
[93] Kao Ling Mei, ed., *Hong Kong* (Kowloon, East Arts Co., 1961), p. 51.
[94] *South China Morning Post,* December 1, 1959. The agreement between China and Great Britain may be found as item No. 1898/11 in John V. A. MacMurray's *Treaties and Agreements with and Concerning China 1894—1919.* (New York, Oxford University Press, 1921) pp. 130—131.

CHAPTER III

PRESENT-DAY ADDICTION

Opium, morphine, heroin, and barbiturates are the drugs which occur most commonly in the illegal traffic in Hong Kong. Occasionally, consumption of other drugs, such as pethidine (sometimes used by members of the medical profession) is found.[1] During my second trip there was also a seizure of a small quantity of cocaine.[2] Actually barbiturates are not commonly used by themselves as narcotics but rather, as a base powder, together with heroin.[3] Thus, the addiction problem primarily centers around the usage of drugs derived from opium.

Origins of the Drug Supply

Only one case of opium growing occurred in the Colony between 1948 and 1963.[4] For all practical purposes, the narcotics consumed in Hong Kong enter the Colony from outside. While most narcotics formerly came from Indian and Persian Gulf ports, practically all opiates now reach Hong Kong by sea or air from Southeast Asian ports, especially from Bangkok (Thailand),[5] usually in the form of raw opium (to be used for opium consumption), morphine or — lately — heroin.[6]

The type of opium most frequently used in Hong Kong — either as opium or as a derivative — is called "Yunnan" opium but this type is produced not only in the Chinese province of Yunnan, from which it is named, but also outside of China — in Laos, Thailand, etc.[7] Not much is known about the morphine sources which are believed to exist close to many of the opium growing areas.[8]

Since one often hears how mainland China is one of the main suppliers of narcotics to the United States, it might be expected that this statement would apply so much more to Hong Kong, which lies directly at China's borders. An investigation into this matter, however, was not a principal object of this report. While some opium probably originates in Yunnan province, my impression is that the role of Red China as a supplier of opium or opium derivatives to Hong Kong is not very important. As already pointed out, large crops of poppies are still grown in Southeast Asia, outside Red China's borders. Furthermore, smuggling of narcotics directly across the China-Hong Kong border does not exist according to statements by officials,[9] even though this border is eminently suitable for such smuggling; its many islands, rugged shore and terrain make it a very difficult border to patrol. Indeed, a good deal of other types of "smuggling" takes place across this border, such as smuggling of refugees and of such articles as alcoholic beverages

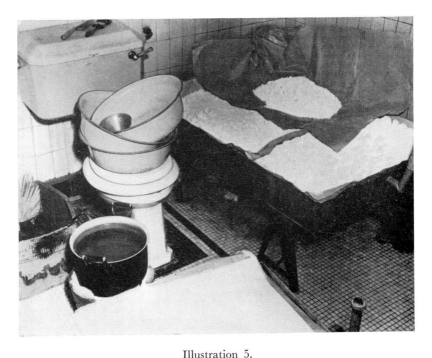

Illustration 5.

HEROIN FACTORY IN THE BATHROOM OF A PRIVATE HOME

The Hong Kong Police found more than 25 lbs. of dangerous drugs in this place.
(Photo H. K. Police Narcotics Bureau, 1959;
Courtesy H.K. Government Information Services)

and tobacco, — those very few products which are subject to customs duty in this free port Colony. If there were extensive smuggling of opiates from China, it would most likely make use of this route.

Clandestine Manufacturing

As we know, heroin is a derivative of morphine, which in turn is extracted from opium. Although certain manufacturing processes are needed for the production of heroin, their technical aspects are simple and can be handled without an elaborate factory setup. Thus, for instance, the Hong Kong authorities sometimes find plants for the production of heroin hidden in bathrooms.[10] (Ill. 5) During my stay in 1961, the newspapers reported two cases in which local manufacture of dangerous drugs had come to the attention of the courts. One case concerned three unemployed men who used the kitchen of a stone hut located in the New Territories. The other case concerned a man from Macau, who made the drugs in an "expensive two-storey house."[11] In 1962, seven heroin laboratories were detected in Hong Kong.[12]

The heroin supply of the Colony was usually manufactured in local plants or in nearby Macau.[13] Of late, however, some of this manufacturing seems to have been shifted to Thailand. In 1961, on my first trip through that country, for example, a heroin plant had just been uncovered in Paknam, Thailand.[14] A year earlier, a secret plant with underground storage had been discovered in Bang Sue; the leader, whose name was Mong, was still allegedly at large in Bangkok, keeping the business running from a secret hideout.[15] Malaysia has been mentioned more recently as a country where heroin was manufactured illegally.[16]

Seizures

Table I lists the quantities of those dangerous drugs seized in Hong Kong while being imported, exported, or in transit. These figures are most striking in their great variations. For example, seizures of opium dropped about 41 % between 1958/9 and 1959/60, but by the following year again rose 66 %, almost equalling the amount for 1958/9. For morphine, the quantity seized rose 312 % from 1959/60 tot 1960/61.

Actually the number of kilos seized depends not only on the efforts, the efficiency, and enthusiasm of the law enforcement agencies, but also

TABLE I

DANGEROUS DRUGS SEIZED IN HONG KONG *

(In kilograms)

Year	Opium	Morphine	Heroin	Barbitone
1958/59	984.744	64.294	36.978	101.101
1959/60	582.76	64.923	54.078	137.957
1960/61	966.27	202.782	63.907	not listed

* Compiled from Hong Kong Commissioner of Police, *Annual Departmental Reports.*

on "battle luck". One seizure, for instance, can at one time yield a large quantity of narcotics and at another time only a small amount. Thus the above figures for total quantities seized do not in their variability necessarily represent the amount of actual smuggling being done or the con-

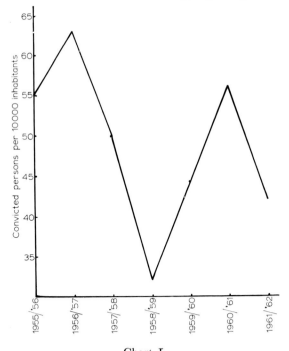

Chart I.

PERSONS CONVICTED FOR NARCOTICS OFFENSES BY HONG KONG MAGISTRACIES PER
10 000 INHABITANTS (1955/56—1961/62)

sumption of the various drugs. Then too, that tremendous "dark figure" which is the difference between the quantities seized and those actually existing in Hong Kong, has yet to be made known. No doubt, a good part of the rise in quantity of narcotics seized from 1960 to 1961 can be explained somewhat, by the stricter legal provisions then introduced and by the special anti-narcotics drive of 1960, when law enforcement was considerably strengthened. What morphine is found is hardly ever destined to be consumed directly in Hong Kong, but to be used as raw materials for the manufacture of heroin. For this reason, the proportionate quantities of various drugs seized do not offer any idea as to the amount of their relative consumption.

As far as potency of each drug is concerned, it should be borne in mind that the number of kilograms can often be misleading. Morphine is about six to ten times as potent as opium, and heroin about five to eight times as potent as morphine.[17]

Hong Kong heroin is high grade material, and in general 65—90 % pure. It comes in packages containing 20 or 40 mgs. Often another package of 100—200 mgs of barbitol is furnished with it.[18]

Trend of Narcotics Offenses

Table II shows the number of persons convicted for narcotics offenses in Hong Kong Magistrates Courts from 1955/56 to 1960/61. Unfortunately, the figures do not distinguish between addict offenders, and traffickers.

TABLE II

PERSONS CONVICTED FOR NARCOTICS OFFENSES IN HONG KONG MAGISTRATES COURTS *

Year	Convicted Persons
1955/56	12 944
1956/57	15 454
1957/58	12 994
1958/59	8 834
1959/60	12 707
1960/61	16 603
1961/62	14 223

* Compiled from the Hong Kong Registrar of the Supreme Court, *Annual Departmental Reports*.

Looking at these raw figures, then, we find a certain amount of fluctuation. Starting out in 1955/56, the number of persons convicted was approximately 12 900, it then sank to 8 800 in 1958, and, through the years, rose again to reach about 16 600 in 1960/61.

As we know, raw crime figures are often misleading because they do not account for changes in the population. For this, one must study the "crime rates", which relate the crime figures to fluctuations in the population figures.

TABLE III

PERSONS CONVICTED FOR NARCOTICS OFFENSES BY HONG KONG MAGISTRATES COURTS
(Per 10 000 Inhabitants)*

Year	Convicted Persons	Rate per 10 000 Inhabitants **
1955/56	12 944	55
1956/57	15 454	63
1957/58	12 994	50
1958/59	8 834	32
1959/60	12 707	44
1960/61	16 603	56
1961/62	14 223	42

* Prepared from various *Annual Departmental Reports*.
** All rates and percentages in this and the following tables were calculated with a slide rule. The degree of accuracy of the figures obtained by that method seemed sufficient for this study.

The rate of convictions per 10 000 Hong Kong inhabitants are given in Table III and are graphically represented in Chart I. In 1955/56, the conviction rate for narcotics offenses was 55 per 10 000 inhabitants. This fluctuating figure rose to 63 in 1956/57, declined to about one-half (to 32) in 1958/59, only to climb again to 56 in 1960/61, or just slightly above the rate for 1955/56, and in the last available year, 1961/62, fell to 43.

In interpreting these crime rates, one also has to bear in mind the legal changes which have taken place during the last few years. In 1958, barbitones were placed on the list of dangerous drugs and the scope of narcotics offenses was repeatedly widened by further amendments to the dangerous drug legislation. These revisions no doubt account partly for the number of rise in crime rate between 1958 and 1961. Furthermore, as mentioned above, the Government of Hong Kong has, since 1959, been sponsoring an anti-narcotics drive. Such a drive generally leads to intensified law enforcement for a while and to more arrests and convictions, without necessarily indicating an increase in criminal activity or narcotics consumption. Thus, as revealed by the rates for 1955 to 1962, the overall picture appears not too alarming; the rates fluctuate but do not show an increase, — rather a slight decrease in spite of the drive and the continuously widening scope of the criminal law provisions.

Number of Addicts

How many drug addicts are there at the present time in Hong Kong? No reliable information about their number is available. According to the *1959 White Paper,* the number lies somewhere between 150 000 and 250 000.[19] An article in an Hong Kong periodical recently suggested a figure of 300 000.[20] A circular of the Society for the Aid and Rehabilitation of Drug Addicts, issued around the same time, states that "one out of fifteen of the adult population of Hong Kong are drug addicts"[21]; this means that about 100 000 adults were then addicts. Recently, the Government has been inclined to consider the number of addicts in Hong Kong lower than the figure of 150 000 given in the *1959 White Paper.*[22] To my knowledge, no new estimates have been made, but unofficially, an estimated number of only 50 000 was mentioned to me. The *1959/60 Progress Report* states that there are "certainly some thousands of addicts and purveyors".[23] Prison statistics reveal that approximately two-thirds of the inmates are addicts, but, actually, this high rate cannot be used as a basis for a generalization with respect to the population at large.[24]

The Use of Opium, Morphine and Heroin

Along with the existing uncertainty about the total number of addicts in Hong Kong, there is uncertainty about the number of those addicted to specific drugs, i.e., to opium, morphine, and heroin. As stated before, morphine plays a very minor role in direct consumption so that, in Table IV, the number of morphine offenses for 1958 through 1961 falls into only the one-digit or two-digit brackets, or only about one-tenth of one per cent of all the offenses involving opiates. Opium offenses amount to between 28 % and 50 %, heroin offenses to between 50 % and 72 %

— suggesting a 1 : 2 ratio in the consumption of opium and heroin. Of 8 505 "known addicts" (which concept is not to be confounded with the "total number" of addicts in a given year), 1776 used opium, 19 morphine, and 6 710 heroin.[25] Here the ratio of heroin users is close to 80 per cent. Lately, an increase in seizures of opium has again been observed, after the use of that drug had been decreasing for a number of years.[26]

Actually, no strict line divides heroin use from opium use, since, according to our survey described below, more than one-half of the addicts consumed either drug at one time or another. Among the Victoria group of 94, 45 % (42) claimed that they had used only one drug; of the 500 addicts in Tai Lam, 37 % (184) made the same claim.

TABLE IV

OFFENSES IN HONG KONG FOR SPECIFIC OPIATES *

Year	Opium		Morphine		Heroin		Total	
	Number	%	Number	%	Number	%	Number	%
1958	3 347	31	9	—	7 617	69	10 973	100
1959	3 630	28	10	—	9 467	72	13 107	100
1960	7 004	40	7	—	10 447	60	17 458	100
1961 (1st half)	4 015	59	9	—	4 054	50	8 078	100

* Courtesy, Bureau of Narcotics, Hong Kong Police Department.

The question of which drug is being used is a matter of availability, preference and price. From a practical viewpoint, heroin can be handled much more easily. Since it is also much more potent,[27] it is used in relatively small quantities, thus making the transportation of heroin easier for the trafficker than the transportation of opium. Further, heroin does not have the typical opium smell which easily betrays the place where the drug is being manufactured.[28] Then, too, from the consumer's viewpoint, it does not require all the complicated paraphernalia which opium-smoking makes necessary. Most decisive, however, is its price. From time to time, inmates of Tai Lam prison who had used both drugs were asked why they had changed from opium to heroin. The standard answer was that heroin was cheaper.

Methods of Drug Consumption

Whenever opium is used, the traditional methods of smoking are employed. For heroin, however, the injection method so common in the United States is not popular in the Colony. One of my sources claimed that it was mainly limited to "go-down", i.e., warehouse coolies in a certain district in Victoria. Our own survey shows seamen relatively often among those who inject.[29] The usual method of heroin consumption is through inhalation, described by the *1959 White Paper* as follows:

"The majority of local addicts smoke heroin by a method called 'chasing the dragon' or by its variant 'playing the mouth organ'. To smoke the drug by the former method, several granules of heroin are mixed with a base powder in a folded piece of tinfoil, which is heated by a taper, the resulting fumes being inhaled through a small tube of bamboo or rolled paper. The fumes move up and down the

Illustration 6.
UTENSILS FOR OPIUM SMOKING
Bamboo pipe, lamp for heating, pipe scraper, opium pots.
(Photo H.K. Police Narcotics Bureau, 1959;
Courtesy H.K. Government Information Services)

tinfoil through with the movements of the molten powder and resemble the undulating tail of the dragon in Chinese mythology. The use of a narrow tube to inhale the fumes is relatively inefficient and a match box cover is often substituted for it. This latter variation is called 'playing the mouth organ' because the inhaling action is very like that of a mouth organ player. A third but less common method is to imbed some granules of heroin in the tip of a cigarette which is lit and held in a vertical position, while the smoker inhales the fumes. The use of heroin in this manner is called 'firing the ack-ack gun'."[30]

Illustrations 6 and 7, show implements used for the smoking of the two drugs. As one can see the paraphernalia for heroin smoking are much simpler; most of them can be made from cigarette wrappings and a

Illustration 7.
UTENSILS FOR HEROIN SMOKING
Pellets, tin foil on which pellets are heated, lamp, tube for inhaling. A taper (r.) is frequently used instead of a lamp.
(Photo H.K. Police Narcotics Bureau, 1959;
Courtesy H.K. Government Information Services)

matchbox. Not even the lamp is necessary for heating the pellets, a paper taper or a match suffices.

The "Divans"

As is well known, opium is frequently taken in so-called opium "dens", which in Hong Kong are locally called "divans". Usually, they are public places in which, for a fee, the management will provide the addict with the drug and implements for its consumption. The *raison d'être* for this institution lay originally in the addict's need for the special paraphernalia and complicated preparations that accompany opium-smoking. With heroin replacing opium, there is hardly any need for such a place. In fact, the addict who consumes the drug in a divan probably exposes himself to police raids and arrests more often than if he takes the drug in isolation.[31] However, the tradition is still continued in Hong Kong and, at the time of my visits there were a sufficient number of heroin divans in operation to attract the attention of the press.[32] In questioning some former addicts as to why divans were still being used, I received the reply that some addicts consider heroin consumption in a divan as a social gathering, where they can carry on a conversation while under the effect of the drug. Others whom I questioned claimed that addicts frequently wished to hide their drug usage from their families.

In the past, Chinese opium dens were sometimes luxurious places. Now Hong Kong's divans are usually found in Hong Kong slums, e.g., in the Old Walled City of Kowloon. Illustration 8 shows such a divan. I understand that this photo, which I obtained through the courtesy of the Hong Kong Government Information Service, was taken during an actual raid, only a moment before the addicts became aware that they were being raided. The room shown is of approximately the same size and type as those which I saw used as ordinary dwellings for large families in the slum areas of the Old Walled City of Kowloon. Indeed, in view of the fact that every inch of living space is commonly used to the fullest extent, it is quite likely that this divan was not exclusively used for administering narcotics but also served as living and sleeping quarters for a number of people. Thus, a small boy is visible in the upper right-hand corner of Illustration 8.

Recently locations of divans have shifted from the slum quarters to

Illustration 8.
NARCOTICS DIVAN IN HONG KONG
(Note small boy in upper right corner.)
(Photo H.K. Police Narcotics Bureau, 1959;
Courtesy H.K. Government Information Services)

the squatter areas, where they are frequently hidden in undergrowth[33]
(Ill. 9).

Secret Societies and Other Forms of Organized Trafficking

In Hong Kong, certain organizations exist which, among other unlawful activities, "protect" the divans and practice drug traffic. As in
other places, illegal syndicates are believed to be behind the scenes of
international traffic. In South East Asia, such trafficking

> "is carried out by complex and efficient 'rings' often including
> persons of different nationalities. This fact has been brought to the
> attention of governments by enforcement authorities of China

Illustration 9.

HEROIN DIVAN BUILT OF BAMBOO AND MATTING IN DENSE UNDERGROWTH ON A
HILLSIDE
(Photo H.K. Police Narcotics Bureau, 1959;
Courtesy H.K. Government Information Services)

(Taiwan), Japan, Hong Kong, Macau, Malaya, Singapore, Thailand
and Viet-Nam. The opium and opiates traffic in the region is no
longer the work of small isolated traffickers but of large organizations with impressive means at their disposal, such as high-
powered cars and speedboats. In jungle and mountainous areas,
opium convoys with armed men have been reported."[34]

On the *local* scene are found smaller groups, and especially the
traditional "secret societies,"[35] sometimes called "triad societies" in
English because of their belief in the association between Heaven, Earth
and Man. Founded in China during the Ching Dynasty (1644—1912),
inspired by patriotic anti-Manchu aims and protected by an elaborate

ritual which usually includes an oath of blood brotherhood, these societies in the course of time became criminal in nature, indulging more recently in such enterprises as the sale of black market theatre tickets, the corruption of Government servants, extortion, property offenses, and the offer of paid "protection" to hawkers, rickshaw-coolies, private car-for-hire drivers, shoeshine boys, prostitutes, dance-hall girls, and restaurants. In 1958 the total revenue of the Triad societies was estimated "in the region of forty million (Hong Kong) dollars."[36] In the same year it was estimated that every sixth inhabitant of Hong Kong is, at least, a nominal member of a triad society,[37] and that these societies had made more than H. K. $ 20 000 a day from the sale and distribution of narcotics.[38]

According to the Police Commissioner's *Annual Departmental Report* for 1960/61, the triad societies "continue to operate in rackets such as trafficking in dangerous drugs ......"[39] Hopeful signs may be found in the observation of the same report that triad societies seem to be splitting up into smaller groups.[40] This hope finds itself strengthened by figures showing the number of police records for the offense of membership in unlawful societies, viz:

1959/60	3 521
1960/61	747
1961/62	301 [41]

The 1961/62 Police *Report,* while stating that "triad societies still continue to be a matter for concern", does not include narcotics offenses among its list of "main offenses committed by Triad members", and states that "triad activity generally remained at a low level."[42]

In January 1963, police officials expressed the opinion that the protection of divans was afforded by comparatively small groups of triad criminals who are frequently in conflict with each other. The societies are considered to be in a state of disorganization, their influence having been much reduced. Little or no use is made of the elaborate triad ritual for initiation or promotion purposes and no triad emblems are worn. The amount of money now extorted from the public or derived from vice operation by individual triad members or the small triad gangs still operating is believed much less than in 1958.

Officials stressed that, although many persons engaged in narcotics traffic may be triad members, they are not necessarily operating as such when pushing drugs. Triad membership may often be incidental to drug trafficking.

During my second stay, I counted in the Hong Kong press six court cases within three weeks involving triad society membership. Only one of them had to do with narcotics; the accused had in 1961 demanded "money from opium divan operators in the Walled City." [43]

Maybe organized crime is moving away from the traditional triad society pattern and preferring more "informal" groupings. During my 1963 visit, one important group of traffickers was arrested. To judge from newspaper reports, the persons involved were not implicated as triad members. Accused were eleven persons, among them two women, to "conspire with others not in custody in dealing in heroin." According to an addict witness (whose testimony should be taken with reservation), the organization consisted of "sellers", "deliverers" and "money collectors"; the members of the ring had to work twelve hours a day. Evidence of the group's illegal activities in the form of films taken by the police played an important role in the proceedings. [44]

The presence of well organized trafficking — whether or not in the form of the triads — usually makes itself felt, it seems, by the ease with which narcotics may be obtained in a particular place. During both my stays in Hong Kong, heroin appeared to be easily procurable in spite of the existing restrictions. To be sure, it was not offered to visiting tourists, but Chinese residents can buy it without great effort, — for example, from street vendors or dance-hall girls (which occupations, incidentally, are widely controlled by the triad societies).

Secret societies and other professional traffickers may also have a hand in smuggling drugs into prison facilities. Talks with some former inmates of the large maximum-security prison at Stanley seem to indicate that, in a general way secret societies may play an important role within the "inmate society".

On the day of my visit to Stanley, seventeen prisoners were confined to solitary disciplinary punishment. I learned that ninety percent of this disciplinary punishment is usually inflicted for the illegal possession of drugs in prison. This state of affairs seems to be limited more or less to

Stanley Prison, which institution I understand, the Prison Department intends to replace with smaller, and mostly open institutions. I found no similar indications of smuggling-in at Tai Lam prison for narcotics addicts.

The Hong Kong Addict — Introductory Remarks

I should now like to present as much of a picture as possible of the addict population of the Colony. Since, to my knowledge, no detailed study of Hong Kong drug abusers has yet been made, I shall only be able to skim the surface in this task. For one thing, only a fraction of the addicts come to the attention of the authorities: and about those who do not come to their attention, little is known. Furthermore, my limited stays did not permit me to undertake an extensive survey, so that this discussion will depend mainly on the limited statistics and documentary material available to me. Most of this documentary material, I might add, deals with addict inmates of Hong Kong prisons. The reader is no doubt aware that, of the criminal statistics compiled by the police, the court, and the correctional administration, the correctional statistics are generally considered least representative of the entire offender population, since prison statistics cover only those relatively few offenders who actually undergo a penalty of imprisonment after being convicted. Thus, those who never come to the authorities' attention are excluded from the statistics. Also excluded are those who, while maintaining police or court contacts, have not entered prison either because they were dropped from the criminal proceedings for one reason or another or because they did not receive a disposition of commitment to a correctional institution. The statistical material presented below should be weighed in the light of the foregoing remarks.

Documentation Used

Through the courtesy of the Hong Kong Prison Department, I was able to collect data from two prisons — Tai Lam and Victoria. At both places data were taken from the excellent prison medical records which in Hong Kong were the type of records where a good deal of information could be found conveniently in one place. Naturally these data had originally been assembled for the specific use of the medical services and not for me, so that very understandably certain information which would have been desirable for this particular study was not always present in the same file. To be sure, a minute search elsewhere might have yielded additional information, but the time limitations of my visits did not permit such a search for the over 5 000 cases of which my material originally consisted. Thus, as an example, the work books at Tai Lam prison did not list an inmate's offenses and penalties. Despite these shortcomings, though, the data are not without interest; many variables and their correlations are here dealt with for the first time. By going through the medical records for one week of intake at H. M. Prison (Victoria) the remand institution for men, I was able to compile the first set of data. The records of all convicted drug users who had entered the prison during the week of October 17, 1961, are included, except for a few records which, for administrative reasons, were not available. [45] Ninety-five cases are included altogether. At the time, no larger sample was available at the prison because inmates generally left Victoria prison, accompanied by their records, within a very short time after their conviction.

While the first set of data was assembled from individual medical records, the second set was obtained from certain work books about inmates at H. M. Prison (Tai Lam), a special institution for drug addicts. One important reason for using these work books was that they contained compilations of data on over 5 000 addicts and could easily be microfilmed for study after my return to America. Originally, I had intended to process the data on all these inmates, but later found this impracticable. Thus, for this report, I limited myself to the last 502 entries. In this group, prisoner No. 6025, who had been convicted on May 15, and then admitted to Tai Lam on May 25, 1961, was the earliest admission and prisoner No. 6526, who was convicted on August 29 and admitted to Tai Lam on September 7, 1961, was the latest. Two of the 502 prisoners were, as it turned out, non-addicts sent to that specialized institution in error and so were eliminated from the study. Thus, I was working with 500 cases.

The type of data collected at Tai Lam and Victoria are partly similar; both list the prisoner's number, age, occupation, length of addiction to opium or heroin (according to the inmates' own admission), and amount of money spent daily on the drug. The "reason for addiction", as given by the addict, is listed regularly at Tai Lam but less regularly at Victoria, while type of offense, penalty, and previous offenses are available only for the Victoria group.[46] Tai Lam records also indicate place of birth, length of stay in Hong Kong, education, and place where addicted.

Of the two groups of prisoners, at Victoria and Tai Lam, the group at Victoria is, no doubt, less biased statistically. At Victoria, our statistics are based on a regular, and practically complete, weekly random intake; while the prisoners at Tai Lam, as will be shown below, are specially selected according to certain intake provisions and are thus less representative of the general addict population of Hong Kong. However, the Tai Lam group, being so much larger, is better suited to a detailed statistical investigation than the Victoria group.[47]

In certain instances, the differences and similarities of the two groups will be compared, but the reader is again forewarned that the small size of the Victoria sample and the inconsistency of the data prohibit a very detailed investigation. The data from the two prisons will be supplemented by other relevant statistics in the following discussion.

Sex Distribution

Table V shows the number of men and women convicted for narcotics offenses in Hong Kong Magistrates Courts. As can be seen, the number

TABLE V

MEN AND WOMEN CONVICTED IN HONG KONG MAGISTRATES COURTS FOR NARCOTICS OFFENSES
(1955/56—1960/61)*

Year	Men		Women		Total	
	Number	%	Number	%	Number	%
1955/56	12 428	96	516	4	12 944	100
1956/57	15 065	97.5	389	2.5	15 454	100
1957/58	12 600	97	394	3	12 994	100
1958/59	8 566	97	268	3	8 834	100
1959/60	12 268	97	439	3	12 707	100
1960/61	16 072	97	531	3	16 603	100

* From *Annual Departmental Reports*, Registrar of the Supreme Court, Hong Kong.

TABLE VI

HONG KONG POPULATION 20 YEARS AND OVER BY SEX *

	Number	Percent
Male	853 524	51
Female	833 992	49
Total	1 687 516	100

* From *1961 Census*, Vol. 2, table 104, p. 16.

of female drug offenders for the years 1955/56 to 1960/61 ranged from only 2.5 % to 4 % of the total number of offenders. The census figures for 1961 (Table VI), show that females twenty years old or more constituted 49 % of the total adult population,[48] i.e., the proportion of adult men to women is about 1 : 1. Thus, men are convicted for narcotics offenses more than twenty times as often as women.[49] Indeed, the number of male addicts is so overwhelming that any investigation of figures on addiction makes sense only if each sex is taken separately. Therefore, with the exception of the sections devoted to women and juveniles, the following refers to male addicts only.[50]

Age Distribution

No addicts below 20 years of age were found at either Victoria or Tai Lam. In Table VII we have compared the age distribution for three different prison populations with the age distribution of the entire male population of the Colony.[51] The three prison populations we have used consist of our two sample groups (the intake at Victoria during the week of October 17, 1961, and the 500 inmates at Tai Lam during May to September, 1961) and, in order to see whether a change had taken place in the Tai Lam population over the years, the group of Tai Lam prisoners, No. 1350 to No. 1651, who were already in the institution during approximately the second half of 1958.

Although the picture obtained is not very consistent, one observation is universal. When compared with the general population, there are proportionately fewer addicts in their twenties (especially ages 20—24) and proportionately more addicts 50 to 54 years old. At Victoria, the low percentage of addicts in their twenties is compensated by the high per-

TABLE VII

AGE OF THE GENERAL MALE POPULATION AS COMPARED WITH THE AGE OF ADDICT PRISONERS

Age Groups	Male Adult Population of Hong Kong *		Addicts at Victoria Prison		Addicts at Tai Lam Prison (Sample Group No. 6025 to No. 6526)		Addicts at Tai Lam Prison (Early Group No. 1350 to No. 1651)	
	Number	%	Number	%	Number	%	Number	%
20—24	111 242	13	5	5.4	9	2	16	6
25—29	137 216	16	11	11.8	35	7	33	11
30—34	140 885	17	25	26.8	74	15	46	16
35—39	123 332	14	16	17.2	74	15	49	17
40—44	107 321	13	7	7.5	69	14	41	14
45—49	86 523	10	10	10.8	58	12	36	12
50—54	60 078	7	10	10.8	60	12	41	14
55 and over	86 927	10	9	9.7	116	23	28	10
Totals	853 524	100	93	100.0	495	100	290	100

* From *1961 Census*, Vol. 2, p. 24, Table 109.

centages of addicts from 30 to 34, and from 35 to 39 years of age. The percentage of addicts in their early forties, however, is again low. In the sample Tai Lam group studied, the highest percentage of addicts is found in the "55 and over" age bracket, but this does not hold true for the earlier group (No. 1350 to No. 1651) at Tai Lam. This change can probably be attributed to a change in intake policy, whereby, as this specialized institution develops, more and more old prisoners are sent there to benefit from its health-oriented facilities. At this time, no attempt shall be made at explaining the high percentage of addicts in the 50—54 group.

The high figures for addicts in their early thirties at Victoria Prison may be explainable in as much as many addicts in this age group are probably dangerous and are therefore sent to Stanley, the Colony's maximum-security prison, instead of to Tai Lam — but our figures do not warrant more than conjecture.

Length of Drug Use

The narcotics users found in the two prison groups under study had consumed either opium or heroin exclusively, or else they had first taken opium and then changed to heroin. No cases are recorded where the order was in reverse.[52] In both the Tai Lam and Victoria files, the length of time each drug was used is expressed in years (or, very exceptionally, in months) and listed according to the statement made by the prisoner himself while being interviewed by a social worker. Officials considered these statements generally reliable.

I was interested in the total duration of the prisoner's habit, regardless of the drug used. Usually, if he had taken only one drug, no problems arose in estimating the length of time he used it. When he had changed from opium to heroin, however, some doubts arose because the records list the number of years (or sometimes months) each of the two drugs were used, but do not give the total length of addiction. In any event, the records always had a listing "opium first", where both drugs were used. Could the two periods be simply added to each other or was there an overlapping and, if so, to what degree? Conceivably, an addict who changes from opium to heroin can also on occasion revert to opium, a drug which still remains quite popular and easily available in Hong Kong. In order to arrive at answers to these problem questions, the length of addiction of all those who used *both* drugs was computed in the following way.

1. A *maximum* length was established by adding together the lengths of addiction to each drug. Thus, the maximum length of addiction for a person addicted ten years to opium and six years to heroin would be sixteen years.

2. Next, a *minimum* length was established by adding *one year* to the longer of the two periods of addiction. Thus, in the above case, the minimum would be eleven years. The reason for the addition of one year was this: where the files had listed "opium first", a complete overlapping of *two* drugs seemed unlikely; use of opium must have preceded use of heroin for some time — a time that was set arbitrarily at one year for all cases.

3. The mean of these two lengths was then calculated by the usual

method of adding maximum and minimum and dividing the total by two. Thus, the mean in the above case would be 13½. I have used this mean in calculating the length of addiction in those cases where both drugs have been used.

4. In rounding out fractions of years, I tried to avoid exaggerating the length of addiction. Thus, fractions up to and including six months were disregarded; for the purposes of this study, addiction of "two years and six months" was regarded as two years, "two years and nine months" as three years. This procedure was followed for all cases, with one exception. Under this procedure, persons addicted for only a few months would have been eliminated, thus creating the misleading impression that they had never been drug users at all. In order to avoid this kind of wrong impression, drug users of less than a year have been listed under the heading "one year and under".

5. The above mean was calculated only when there were two or more years difference between the maximum and minimum length of addiction. If the difference was less — if, for example, a prisoner had used one of the drugs two years and six months or less — this difference between maximum and minimum length was not considered important enough to warrant calculation of a mean, so that only the maximum length was used.

As shown in Table VIII most of the men (81 % at Tai Lam and 74 % at Victoria) had a history of addiction that ranged from six years on up. Only 19 % in Tai Lam and 26 % in Victoria had taken the drugs for five years or less. Indeed, a few at Tai Lam had been addicted for as

TABLE VIII

LENGTH OF ADDICTION

Length of Addiction	Tai Lam Group		Victoria Group	
	Number	%	Number	%
5 years or less	94	19	24	26
6—10 years.	132	27	33	35
11—15 years	99	20	18	19
16—20 years	56	12	10	11
21 years or more	105	22	8	9
Total	486	100	93	100

many as 50 years, and at Victoria for as much as 33 years. The shortest
lengths of drug usage recorded were two months for a drug user at Tai
Lam and three months for one at Victoria.

The mean length of addiction was calculated at 14 years at Tai Lam
and 10.4 years at Victoria. Not only is the mean length of addiction
somewhat longer at Tai Lam, but this institution also has a much higher
percentage (22 per cent) of prisoners who were addicted for 21 years or
more, than does Victoria, where only 9 % have been addicted that long.
Both of these observations are apparently related to the large number of
older addicts at Tai Lam.

TABLE IX

TAI LAM PRISONERS ACCORDING TO AGE AND LENGTH OF ADDICTION

Age Groups		Length of Addiction					
		5 yrs. or less	6—10 years	11—15 years	16—20 years	21 yrs. or more	Totals
25 yrs. or	Number	9	5	—	—	—	14
less	%	64	36	—	—	—	100
26—30	Number	21	17	5	—	—	43
years	%	49	39	12	—	—	100
31—35	Number	20	40	12	2	—	74
years	%	27	54	16	3	—	100
36—40	Number	14	25	23	11	1	74
years	%	19	34	31	15	1	100
41—45	Number	10	22	20	9	3	64
years	%	16	34	31	14	5	100
46—50	Number	7	13	16	12	16	64
years	%	11	20	25	19	25	100
51—55	Number	5	4	9	14	18	50
years	%	10	8	18	28	36	100
56 yrs. or	Number	8	6	14	8	67	103
more	%	8	6	13.5	8	64.5	100
Total	Number	94	132	99	56	105	486
	%	19	27	20	12	22	100

As one might expect, a comparison of the length of addiction with the
age distribution at Tai Lam prison shows that the older the age group,
the higher the percentage of those with a long history of addiction
(Table IX). [53] Nevertheless, cases of short addiction are not entirely
unknown in the older age group. Thus, of the Tai Lam addicts 56 years
old or more, 8 % had been addicts for 5 years or less.

Age When First Addicted

By means of the procedure outlined above, the approximate age at which addiction started can be calculated (See Table X).

TABLE X

PRISONERS ACCORDING TO THE APPROXIMATE AGE WHEN FIRST ADDICTED

Age When First Addicted	Tai Lam		Victoria	
	Number	%	Number	%
20 years or less	50	10	11	12.0
21—25 years	121	25	25	27.2
26—30 years	106	22	26	28.3
31—35 years	96	20	14	15.1
36—40 years	54	11	10	10.9
41—45 years	19	4	2	2.2
46—50 years	25	5	3	3.3
51—55 years	10	2	1	1.1
56 years or more	5	1	—	—
Total	486	100	92	100.1

TABEL XI

TAI LAM PRISONERS WHO BECAME ADDICTED AT THE AGE OF 20 OR LESS

Age When Addicted	Number	%
10	1	2
11	—	—
12	1	2
13	—	—
14	—	—
15	7	14
16	4	8
17	5	10
18	7	14
19	11	22
20	14	28
Total	50	100

Most men (47 per cent at Tai Lam, 55.5 per cent at Victoria) first became addicted in their twenties although quite a number started when they were 31 to 35 years old. Taken together, these ages account for 67 per cent and 70 per cent of the two prison populations. At Tai Lam, 10 per cent, and at Victoria 12 per cent had already turned to narcotics at the age of twenty or less. A breakdown of this group of 10 per cent (or 50 cases) at Tai Lam is presented in Table XI. It will be noted that 50 per cent became addicted at the ages of 19 and 20.

Amount Spent on Drugs

Table XII shows the amount which addicts at Tai Lam and Victoria claimed they spent each day on their drugs. Prison officials considered these statements generally reliable.

TABLE XII

AMOUNT SPENT DAILY BY ADDICTS ON NARCOTICS
(in Hong Kong Dollars)★

	Addicts			
Amount Spent Daily	Tai Lam		Victoria	
	Number	%	Number	%
$ 5 or less.	183	37.5	35	38
$ 6—$ 10	206	42.1	44	47
$ 11—$ 15.	83	16.9	8	9
$ 16 or more	18	3.5	6	6
Total	490	100.0	93	100.0

★ One H.K. Dollar = approximately 17½ U.S. cents.

As can be seen in Table XII, a little over one-third in each group of prisoners spent five Hong Kong dollars (about 88 cents in the United States) or less per day. Four-fifths did not spend more than ten dollars (about $ 1.75 in the United States) daily. It would be misleading to compare these amounts at face value with American narcotics prices, which, as is well known, are much higher. For example, New York City's Mayor Robert F. Wagner recently estimated that an addict in that city spends about $ 10 000 a year, or $ 27.50 a day on heroin — or sixteen to thirty-one times what Hong Kong addicts will spend.[55] The difference in buying power of the two countries has to be taken into consideration.

For the sake of comparison, the reader should refer to the wages earned by residents of Hong Kong: unskilled workers receive a daily wage of roughly 5 Hong Kong dollars; but most drug users in the Colony spend up to twice this amount. Using the comparable hourly wage of $ 1.25 in the United States, the New York City addict, according to Mayor Wagner's estimate, will each day spend roughly three to four working day's wages on his addiction.

Table XIII compares the average amount spent by Tai Lam prisoners with the length of addiction of the prisoners. The mean amount spent by addicts at Victoria was H. K. $ 7.70 and for Tai Lam H. K. $ 7.72. In making up the averages for column A, four exceptional cases in which $ 25 or more was spent daily on the drug, were eliminated in order to avoid undue weighting (Column A). In this more reliable Column A, the amount of money spent on drugs rose in relation to the rise in the length of addiction for the first 15 years only. From that point, the amount spent declines, first gradually, then rapidly, until it reaches a level only slightly higher than that for the group addicted for five years or less ($ 5.70). For those who were addicted for only one year or less, the daily amount spent was H. K. $ 5.15. There may have been a number of occasional drug users among this group who were not yet "addicts" in the strict sense of the word.

TABLE XIII

MEAN AMOUNT SPENT DAILY ON DRUGS AS COMPARED TO LENGTH OF ADDICTION
Tai Lam Group

Length of Addiction	A	B
5 years or less	H.K. $ 5.70	H.K. $ 5.81
6—10 years.	7.65	7.95
11—15 years	8.36	8.36
16—20 years	8.26	9.33
21—25 years	8.20	8.20
26—30 years	7.60	7.60
31 years or more	6.12	6.69

A = Mean calculated after elimination of four prisoners, of whom two spent
    H.K. $ 25 each daily, one spent H.K. $ 30 and the other spent H.K. $ 50.
B = Mean calculated with inclusion of the four exceptional cases.

The figures for those addicted for up to 15 years appears to reflect the building-up of their "tolerance", the well-known phenomenon of having to increase drug consumption more and more as the effects of the drug are lessened.[56] After fifteen years, however, this "tolerance" no longer plays a statistically significant role — or else the figures would continue to rise *ad infinitum*. But what are the reasons for this "levelling off"?

As Table IX indicated, the men with a longer history of addiction were usually the older ones. Is this decrease, or levelling off, in consumption connected with their aging (which, as is sometimes believed, may play a physiological or psychological role in diminishing the bases of addiction)?[57]

TABLE XIV

AGE OF TAI LAM ADDICTS COMPARED WITH MEAN DAILY SPENDING

Age	A	B
25 years old or less	6.60	6.60
26—30 years old	8.45	8.84
31—35 years old	8.70	8.97
36—40 years old	8.40	8.95
41—45 years old	7.92	7.92
46—50 years old	7.46	7.46
51—55 years old	7.13	7.50
56—60 years old	5.90	5.90
61 years old or more	5.13	5.60

A = Mean calculated after elimination of 4 prisoners, of whom two spent $ 25 each, one spent $ 30, and the other spent $ 50.
B = Mean calculated with the inclusion of the four exceptional cases.

Table XIV shows the relationship between the age of Tai Lam addicts and the amount of money spent daily on drugs. In the youngest and oldest age brackets, the amount spent daily is small; in the 26—30 and 31—40 age brackets, the amount spent is at its peak.

Later in this chapter, we shall return to these variables of length of addiction and age when addicted.

Occupational Status

Table XV, then, shows the occupations of drug users sent to Tai Lam and Victoria. Basically, the picture is very similar for prisoners at both institutions and also resembles the breakdown presented in the *White Paper*.[58] Very few addicts worked at commercial or professional occupations (1.6 per cent and 3 per cent respectively). Nearly one-half of the addicts were unskilled laborers, one-fourth were skilled workers, and one-fifth were engaged in such "street" occupations as hawking. The remainder were fishermen, farmers, and seamen. Unfortunately, we cannot compare these figures with those for the occupations of the general population, since the categories of the *1961 Census* are too differently structured to be used as a basis for a comparison.[59] We may, however, assume that among drug users, low-status groups are those most strongly represented. As the *1959 White Paper* notes still further, many addicts who may have formerly held higher positions, may now hold inferior jobs as a result of their addiction.[60] As can be seen from Table XV, about 70 per cent of the addicted prisoners belonged to three groups: the jobless, the unskilled and the hawkers (a street occupation) — groups of persons who, according to the *1959 White Paper,* live and work under "wretched conditions."[61]

TABLE XV

OCCUPATIONS OF ADDICTS

	Tai Lam		Victoria	
	Number	%	Number	%
Unemployed	13	2.6	4	4.0
Street Occupations	88	17.6	14	15.0
Unskilled Laborers	245	49.1	42	45.0
Skilled Laborers	120	24.1	26	28.0
Commerce and Professions	8	1.6	3	3.0
Fishermen and Farmers	23	4.6	5	5.0
Seamen	2	0.4	—	—
Total	499	100.0	94	100.0

Table XVI shows the occupational status of the Tai Lam population by age groups. In most occupations, the figures for each age group are too small to be significant. However, the relation of skilled to unskilled occupations for prisoners 26 to 30 years old, viz. 49 % : 30 % is rather interesting, because it is a reversal of Table XV where a ratio of 24 % : 49 % skilled to unskilled, within the total Tai Lam population was indicated. The Victoria population is too small to compare in this manner as are the Tai Lam addicts 25 years old or less, although for the latter the percentages for the skilled and unskilled workers are nearly even (45 % : 55 %). If there are really more skilled workers among the younger addicts — a fact that would require further ascertaining — two explanations may particularly be taken into consideration:

1. More users of narcotics may be coming recently from the higher-level occupational groups, thus changing the addict population, or

2. The good occupational status of the younger addicts may signify that they are still in a better position than the older ones to function in skilled jobs. The youngest addicts, as we have seen, have also had the shortest period of addiction. Thus, there may not yet be as much of the alleged deterioration of the addict.

In this connection, a word may also be said on the number of unem-

TABLE XVI

AGE AND OCCUPATIONS OF TAI LAM ADDICTS

Age		Unem-ployed	Street Occupa-tions	Un-skilled Workers	Skilled Workers	Com-merce and Pro-fessions	Fisher-men and Farmers	Sea-men	Total
rs. or less	No.	—	4	5	4	1	1	—	15
	%	—	26.5	33.0	26.5	7.0	7.0	—	100
-30 yrs.	No.	2	5	13	21	1	1	—	43
	%	5.0	12.0	30.0	49.0	2.0	2.0	—	100
-35 yrs.	No.	2	9	38	18	1	6	—	74
	%	3.0	12.0	51.5	24.5	1.0	8.0	—	100
-40 yrs.	No.	3	9	46	16	—	2	—	76
	%	4.0	12.0	60.5	21.0	—	2.5	—	100
-45 yrs.	No.	1	11	30	18	1	3	1	65
	%	1.5	17.0	46.0	27.5	1.5	5.0	1.5	100
-50 yrs.	No.	1	16	34	11	2	3	—	67
	%	1.5	24.0	50.5	16.5	3.0	4.5	—	100
-55 yrs.	No.	—	9	26	13	—	2	—	50
	%	—	18.0	52.0	26.0	—	4.0	—	100
yrs. or ver	No.	4	24	50	19	2	5	1	105
	%	4.0	23.0	47.0	18.0	2.0	5.0	1.0	100
un-nown	No.	—	1	3	—	—	—	—	4
	%	—	25.0	75.0	—	—	—	—	100
al	No.	13	88	245	120	8	23	2	499
	%	2.6	17.6	49.1	24.1	1.6	4.6	0.4	100

ployed who amount to 2.6 % at Tai Lam and 4 % at Victoria (Table XV). While, as we had seen, we cannot compare the occupational figures for our groups with those of the general Hong Kong population, a glance at the Hong Kong unemployment statistics may be of interest. The *1961 Census* lists 11 798 unemployed male workers 20 years and over. With a male population in the same age brackets of 853 524, the unemployed amount to 1.4 per cent.[62] Thus, the percentages of unemployed appear to be higher among the drug users.[63] Still, one may also be inclined to look somewhat differently at these figures: for groups, generally considered to be "deteriorated", it may be quite remarkable to have over 95 % employed, especially if one also takes into account that there are four persons, fifty-six years and over, in the Tai Lam group (Table XVI).

Education

The two explanations mentioned in the preceding section may also be studied in light of the educational level attained by the addict prisoners. Table XVII gives an educational picture of Tai Lam addicts. Over one-fourth are either illiterate or had one year or less of education (130). Of these, 95, or 19 per cent of the total, were listed as completely illiterate; 15 per cent had 9 or more years of education. The average was about four years of education.[64]

TABLE XVII

EDUCATIONAL ATTAINMENT OF TAI LAM PRISONERS

Years of Education	Number	%
1 year or less or illiterate .	130	26
2 years	35	7
3 years	72	15
4 years	60	12
5 years	35	7
6 years	48	10
7 years	20	4
8 years	20	4
9 years or more	72	15
Total	492	100

TABLE XVIII

EDUCATIONAL ATTAINMENT OF THE HONG KONG MALE POPULATION 15 YEARS OLD OR MORE *

	Number	%
No Schooling	88 897	10
6 Years **	454 096	52
9 Years and Over *** .	330 177	38
Total	873 170	100

* From *1961 Census*, Vol. II, p. 74, Table 166. Privately tutored persons are omitted from this table.
** Equivalent to what is known in Hong Kong as a primary education.
*** Equivalent to what is known in Hong Kong as a junior middle, lower secondary or higher education.

These educational attainments may be compared with those of the adult male Hong Kong population (Table XVIII), even if the lower age limits do not completely correspond. There were twice as many illiterates among the addict prisoners as in the male population at large. [65] The discrepancy in educational attainment of the addict prisoners at Tai Lam is brought into still greater relief when we compare percentages of those who received five years or less (67 per cent) and

TABLE XIX

OCCUPATIONS OF TAI LAM PRISONERS WITH BRIEF AND EXTENDED EDUCATION

	Years of Education			
Occupation	1 Year or Less		9 Years or More	
	Number	%	Number	%
Unemployed	2	2	2	3
Street Occupations	17	13	17	24
Unskilled Laborers	72	55	33	46
Skilled Laborers.	28	22	12	17
Commerce and Professions	—	—	6	8
Fisherman and Farmers	11	8	1	1
Others and Unknown	—	—	1	1
Seamen	—	—	—	—
Total	130	100	72	100

nine years or more (15 per cent) of education with the general male population of whom at least 90 per cent had completed primary school (or about four years of education) and 38 per cent had completed nine or more years of education.

A comparison of the occupation of Tai Lam prisoners who had a short education with the occupations of addicts with a longer education (Table XIX) shows that all those who had formerly been employed in commercial occupations or professions had had nine or more years of education.[66] Otherwise, and perhaps more remarkable, both groups — those who had a short education and those who had a long one — are quite similar, even when the fact that the relatively small figures do not permit much interpretation is taken into account. The better-educated group did not have a much lower number of unskilled laborers among them and even had fewer skilled laborers than did the group of illiterates or near-illiterates. Street occupations were more frequently recorded for the better-educated group; while nearly all fishermen and farmer addicts were uneducated.[67] By adding the percentages for the three lowest-strata occupational groups (unemployed, street occupations, and un-skilled laborers) for the uneducated and the percentages for the educated in the same occupations we arrive at a relationship of 70 percent to 73 per cent respectively. Thus, the occupational status of the educated addict prisoner is, on the whole, hardly superior to that of the unedu-cated one — a picture that may reflect the general employment situation in Hong Kong or — conceivably — the deterioration of the addict.

No doubt, many Chinese refugees in the general population of Hong Kong are holding extremely menial positions in spite of their good education and without their being addicted to narcotics. According to the *1961 Census,* the percentage of unemployed (including "job seekers") is practically the same for persons with university training as for persons with no schooling whatsoever. (1.7 per cent and 1.5 per cent).[68]

Reasons for Taking Narcotics

The records in both prisons contain brief statements by the prisoners on why they began taking narcotics. In the Tai Lam work books, these statements are practically always recorded, while in the records at Vic-toria, they appear less frequently. Although we do not know to what degree these statements really reflect the addicts' motivations, it may nevertheless be interesting to see whether they show any pattern.

As was said before, according to a Chinese tradition which still exists, opium is considered a cure for all kinds of diseases; by the same tradition it is also considered an aphrodisiac, a means of overcoming fatigue, and so forth. This tradition is reflected in the statements of the addicts, whose reasons, as recorded, can be divided into medical and non-medical ones (Table XX).[69] The figures for addicts at Victoria might in themselves be too small to draw many conclusions from them, but they seem to bear out the figures for addicts at Tai Lam. At Tai Lam, 61 per cent of the reasons given in the addicts' statements were medical ones as

TABLE XX

REASONS GIVEN BY PRISONERS FOR TAKING NARCOTICS

	Tai Lam		Victoria	
	Number	%	Number	%
A. Medical Reasons Recorded				
Gastric and abdominal pain, diarrhea	213	43	18	45
Headache, aches in bones or lumbar region	6	1	—	—
Cough	14	3	—	—
Asthma, breathlessness	12	2	—	—
Chest pain, vomiting blood, tuberculosis, "lung disease"	38	8	2	5
Broken bones, injuries, hernia . .	13	3	1	2.5
Other or unspecified medical reasons	6	1	1	2.5
Total	302	61	22	55.0
B. Nonmedical Reasons Recorded				
Association	156	31	10	25
Overwork, nightwork	24	5	8	20
Sexual stimulus	5	1	—	—
Other reasons (e.g., worries) . . .	8	2	—	—
Total	193	39	18	45
GRAND TOTAL	495	100	40	100

compared to 55 per cent for Victoria addicts. Of these, 43 per cent and 45 per cent, respectively, concerned gastric and abdominal pains and diarrhea. Other medical reasons seldom showed in the statements for either group. Not one statement for addicts in either prison mentioned venereal disease, although it is well known in Hong Kong that narcotics are sometimes used in an attempt — no doubt futile — to cure it.

Among the nonmedical reasons, the one most frequently recorded was "association" (that is social intercourse with friends who were drug users) — 31 per cent for Tai Lam and 21 % for Victoria. In these "association" cases, the drug seems to be taken expressly for the euphoric effect. "Heavy work", the second most frequently recorded nonmedical reason was given relatively more often by the Victoria addicts (20 %) who, as we have seen, have fewer older men among them than those at Tai Lam.

Of course, we do not know whether, and to what degree, the addicts were truthful in making their statements. We can let it be said, however, that the actual physical condition of the men does not seem to contradict their statements. Indeed, it should be noted that although only 11 % of the Tai Lam prisoners gave cough (3 per cent), tuberculosis, chest pains, lung disease, and vomiting blood (8 per cent) as the medical reason for their addiction, among the 915 prisoners discharged from that institution during the first-half of 1961, 194, or 21 per cent, were afflicted with tuberculosis.[70] As to "heavy work", or "overwork", the reader should again consider the description of labor conditions given above in light of this relatively frequently recorded reason.

A breakdown of the reasons according to age groups reveals that the proportion of medical to nonmedical reasons remains approximately the

TABLE XXI

REASONS GIVEN BY TAI LAM PRISONERS FOR TAKING NARCOTICS ACCORDING TO AGE GROUP

Age	Medical Reasons		Nonmedical Reasons	
	Number	%	Number	%
30 years and below	26	45	32	55
31—55 years	212	64	118	36
56 years and above	62	61	40	39

same for both the middle and old-age groups — 64 per cent to 36 per cent and 61 per cent to 39 per cent, respectively, or about a ratio of 6 : 4 (see Table XXI). For those 30 years old or less, the proportion is 45 per cent to 55 per cent. The higher percentage of non-medical reasons given by the younger addicts may indicate that they began taking drugs more frequently for euphoric sensations.

TABLE XXII

REASONS GIVEN BY TAI LAM PRISONERS FOR TAKING NARCOTICS ACCORDING TO EDUCATIONAL LEVEL ATTAINED

Reasons	Educational Level 1 year or less		Educational Level 9 years or more	
	Number	%	Number	%
Medical	77	60	44	63
Nonmedical.	52	40	26	37
Total	129	100	70	100

Another reasonable expectation is that addicts with more education would tend to put less trust in the curative effect of the drug and would be more likely to indicate nonmedical reasons for taking it than would those addicts who had little education. This, however, is not borne out by the figures on Table XXII. The percentages for medical and nonmedical reasons reported are practically the same for both those who are illiterate (or nearly so) and those who had nine years or more of education.

Offenses Committed by the Addict Prisoners

Tai Lam workbooks contain, as already pointed out, no information on the criminal acts committed by the addict prisoners, but the records at Victoria Prison do list both past and present convictions, describe the offense in a few sketchy words, and give the penalty.

The 94 addict-prisoners at Victoria had a total of 344 convictions,[71] the distribution of which is shown on Table XXIII. An offender quite often received only one conviction for several offenses. To avoid counting each conviction several times, certain rules were established as a means of preparing this compilation. First of all, heroin offenses were regarded as taking precedence over other types of narcotics offenses named in the same conviction (offenses such as possession of barbiturates, and use of barbiturates as a base powder for the smoking of heroin).[72] In addition, breaches of police supervision and breaches of bond or deportation orders have been considered subsidiary to other offenses (such as larceny) which may have been mentioned in the same judgement.

TABLE XXIII

OFFENSES FOR WHICH VICTORIA ADDICTS WERE CONVICTED

Type of Conviction	Number of Convictions	%
Opium offenses	86	25
Heroin offenses	132	38
Other or unspecified narcotics offenses .	2	1
Total: All narcotics offenses	220	64
Property offenses (larceny, housebreaking, and related offenses).	87	25
Membership in a secret society	4	1
Breach of bond, not reporting while under police supervision, breach of deportation orders	15	4
Assault and offenses of violence.	3	1
Mendicancy	7	2
Other offenses	8	3
Total: All other offenses	124	36
GRAND TOTAL	344	100

The breakdown on Table **XXIII** shows that all narcotics offenses constituted 64 per cent of the 344 convictions. Of this, 38 per cent of these convictions were for heroin offenses. The relationship between heroin and opium offenses is about 6 to 4. Among those offenses which did not involve drugs, property offenses (i.e., housebreaking, larceny, and related offenses) constituted 25 % of the convictions. Although only one per cent of the convictions were for membership in a secret society, the small percentage hardly reflects the true number of members among the prisoners.

Assault and other offenses of violence constituted an extremely minor part of the total number of convictions — only one per cent — thus bearing out the statement that "opium and its derivatives fortunately do not stimulate to crimes of violence."[73]

TABLE XXIV

LENGTH OF CONVICTION IMPOSED ON ADDICT PRISONERS AT VICTORIA PRISON
(BY TYPE OF OFFENSE)

Type of Offense	Convictions				Total Number of Convictions for Each Type of Offense	
	More than one year		One year or less			
	No.	%	No.	%	No.	%
Heroin offenses	6	4.5	126	95.5	132	100
Other drug offenses . . .	5	6.0	83	94.0	88	100
Total: All drug offenses	11	5.0	209	95.0	220	100
Larceny, burglary, and similar offenses	9	10.0	78	90.0	87	100
Other offenses	0	—	37	100.0	37	100
Total: All other offenses . . .	9	7.0	115	93.0	124	100
GRAND TOTAL.	20	6.0	324	94.0	344	100

Let us now take a look at the length of sentences imposed. According to Table XXIV, 94 per cent (324) of all 344 convictions resulted in imprisonment for one year or less. Convictions for larceny, burglary, and similar offenses that resulted in *more than one year's* imprisonment constituted 10 per cent of the 87 convictions in this category.

As for all drug offenses, only 5 per cent (11 out of 220) received long sentences, quite a different situation from that in the United States, where long minimum sentences are often handed down. This difference in sentencing procedure becomes even more marked when the number of known previous convictions for each prisoner is taken into consideration (Table XXV). Only 18 per cent had no known previous convictions as contrasted with 40 per cent who had 2 to 4 and 22 per cent who had 5 or more convictions.

TABLE XXV

KNOWN PREVIOUS CONVICTIONS OF ADDICTS AT VICTORIA

No. of Known Previous Convictions	No. of Prisoners	%
None	17	18
1	19	20
2—4	38	40
5—7	9	10
8 or more	10	12
Total	93	100

Longer Sentences Provided For

In connection with recent amendments to the legislation concerning dangerous drugs, there are indications of a tendency toward somewhat longer sentences for offenses of trafficking and manufacturing of narcotics. Sections 4 and 5 of the Dangerous Drugs Regulations, for example, contain special sentencing provisions for offenses involving the sale and distribution of dangerous drugs, and section 3 now provides for sentences as severe as life imprisonment for illegal manufacturing of drugs.[74] However, traffickers are not always dealt with under these specialized provisions. Both pushers and users alike are often sentenced under such other sections as Section 17 ff. of the Dangerous Drugs Ordinance and Section 8 of the Dangerous Drugs Regulations.[75] Thus, the convictions do not clearly express a distinction between addict and dealer, but the term of the sentence (which generally is longer when more narcotics are found) may, to some degree, be indicative of a distinction in the difference.

Some "big catches" notwithstanding, the traffickers who come to the attention of the Hong Kong authorities are, as a rule, small-scale pushers. The *1959 White Paper* states: "Both the keepers of divans and the pedlars are invariably men of straw".[76] As far as I can see, no attention has been paid either in special legal provisions or in actual court practice to the specific, and apparently quite acute, problems of the "addict-pusher". To quote from the *1959 White Paper,* traffickers (pedlars and divan keepers) often

"are addicts themselves plying this trade — either on its own or at

the same time as some other street occupation like hawking, rick-
shaw-pulling or prostitution — in order to pay for their own doses
which they could not otherwise afford."[77]

As shown above in Table XXV, 82 per cent of the offenders had one
or more known convictions. But if we compare the number of first and
last convictions for the various offense categories (Table XXVI), we
find that the figures do not support the well-known thesis that drug users
are criminals first and addicts second. (The figures, to be sure, are small
and should be regarded with reservations.) Of the 77 first known convictions, for example, 66 per cent (or 51) were for drug offenses. Only
34 per cent of the convictions were for larceny, burglary, and other
offenses.

TABLE XXVI

ADDICT PRISONERS AT VICTORIA, SENTENCED SEVERAL TIMES, ACCORDING TO THEIR
FIRST AND LAST KNOWN CONVICTIONS

Type of Offense	First Known Conviction		Last Conviction	
	No. of Prisoners	%	No. of Prisoners	%
Heroin offenses	27	35	36	51
Other narcotics offenses	24	31	26	37
Larceny, burglary, etc.	12	16	6	9
Other offenses	14	18	2	3
Total	77	100	70	100

Looking at the changes in figures for the first and last known convictions, we see that the number of larceny and burglary (property)
offenses decreased by half, while the other nondrug offenses were reduced
to one-sixth. This change does not exactly bear out the popular belief
that addicts will become more and more prone to commit crimes in order
to support their habit, because the 22 per cent increase in the number of
persons convicted for all narcotics offenses offsets this decrease.

Birthplace And Place Where Habit Was Taken Up

Table XXVII shows the birthplace for Hong Kong's total male popu-

lation and for the addict prisoners at Tai Lam. As we can see, 91 per
cent of the addicts at Tai Lam were born in China and only 8 per cent
in Hong Kong, while for the total male population, the figures are
nearly even — 50.5 per cent born in China and 47 per cent in Hong
Kong.

TABLE XXVII

BIRTHPLACES OF THE TOTAL MALE POPULATION * AND ADDICT PRISONERS AT
TAI LAM

Birthplace	Total Male Population		Tai Lam Prisoners	
	Number	%	Number	%
Hong Kong	241 492	47.0	39	8.0
China	261 120	50.5	455	91.0
Elsewhere	13 197	2.5	4	1.0
Total	515 809	100.0	498	100.0

* *1961 Census*, Vol. 2, Table 122.

In spite of the fact that nine out of ten addicts were born in China,
this country was not the place where the habit began: 85 per cent of the
men took to narcotics in Hong Kong, as compared to only 15 per cent
who took up drug use in China (Table XXIX).

Let us go back to Table XXVII. In *both* groups — the Tai Lam
addicts and the general population — birthplaces outside China or Hong
Kong are rare. A few were born in nearby Macau, but, statistically
speaking, they do not carry weight. It may be of interest that American
sailors will, on occasion, become involved with narcotics in Hong Kong.
During my stay, for example, an American sailor was brought before the
South Kowloon magistrate for possessing 0.1 grams of heroin and a
syringe fitted with a needle. The defendant was discharged but ordered
to sign a bond for H. K. $ 750, stipulating that he would be on good
behavior for one year. The shipping company by which he was
employed promised to take care of him and arrange for his departure
from Hong Kong. The American Consul-General was quoted to have
said that, as soon the sailor returned to the United States, he would
be tried for the offense.[78]

TABLE XXVIII

LENGTH OF RESIDENCE IN HONG KONG; A COMPARISON OF THE GENERAL MALE
POPULATION * AND TAI LAM PRISONERS BORN OUTSIDE THE COLONY

Length of Residence	General Male ** Population		Tai Lam ** Prisoners	
	Number	%	Number	%
5 years or less. . . .	155 780	19.0	14	3.0
6—11 years	220 264	26.5	93	20.5
12—15 years	223 992	27.0	197	43.0
16 years or more . .	228 100	27.5	152	33.5
Total	828 136	100.0	456	100.0

* 15 years old or more. *1961 Census*, Vol. 3, Table 222, p. 15.
** Non-Hong Kong born only.

Table XXVIII compares the length of residence in Hong Kong of
those within the general male population and at Tai Lam who were
born outside of the Colony.[79] Only 3 per cent of the prisoners at Tai
Lam, as compared to 19 per cent of the general male population, had
resided in Hong Kong for five years or less. The percentage of prisoners
with six to eleven years of residence in the Colony was slightly lower
than for the general male population. On the other hand, the percentage
of addicts with 12 to 15 years' residence in Hong Kong and those with
16 or more years' residence surpassed the percentage for the general male
population (43 per cent as compared to 27 per cent, and 33.5 per cent as
compared to 27.5 per cent).

TABLE XXIX

PLACE WHERE TAI LAM ADDICTS TOOK UP THE HABIT *

Place Where the Habit Was Taken Up	Tai Lam Prisoners	
	Number	%
Hong Kong	413	85
China	75	15
Elsewhere	2	—
Total	490	100

* According to their recorded statements.

Our table does not show this but actually, 65 per cent (294) of the addicts at Tai Lam had been residents of Hong Kong from 10 to 16 years. Only eight per cent (35) had resided there 9 years or less; these two groups — that is 73 per cent altogether — represent the post-World War II immigration. Those who had lived in the Colony from 21 to 62 years comprised 27 per cent (128) of the addicts. When these figures are compared with the average length of addiction, — about 14 years — we find that they coincide quite closely. Thus, most addicts at Tai Lam prison were born in mainland China, had come to the Colony after World War II, and had become addicted shortly after their arrival — facts which point to a close relationship between Hong Kong's refugee and addiction problems.

Persons who arrived more recently in Hong Kong — that is for all practical purposes refugees who had left the Chinese mainland after it had come completely under Communist rule in 1949 — seem to be less inclined towards drug abuse then those who had entered the Colony shortly after World War II. The reasons for this are unknown; further study of this question may be of interest.

Addicts Who Used Only One Drug

I thought it might be interesting to investigate — as far as the small

TABLE XXX

AGE DISTRIBUTION OF ADDICTS WHO USED EITHER HEROIN OR OPIUM, AS COMPARED WITH THE ENTIRE ADDICT GROUP AT TAI LAM PRISON

| Age Group | Narcotic Used | | | | Entire Study Group of Tai Lam Drug Users * | |
| | Heroin Only | | Opium Only | | | |
	No. of Prisoners	%	No. of Prisoners	%	No. of Prisoners	%
20—24 years	5	4	1	2	9	2
25—29 years	26	19	4	9	35	7
30—34 years	41	30	3	7	74	15
35—39 years	24	17	5	12	74	15
40—44 years	18	13	5	12	69	14
45—49 years	9	6	2	5	58	12
50—54 years	6	4	4	9	60	12
55 years or more	10	7	19	44	116	23
Total	139	100	43	100	495	100

* From Table VII, p. 54.

figures permit — those Tai Lam prisoners who had used only one drug, either heroin or opium. For the purposes of comparison, Table XXX shows their age distribution, together with the ages of our entire addict study group at Tai Lam.

In all three groups, there are very few prisoners 20 to 24 years old. Not unexpectedly, the percentage of the heroin-only users is remarkably high in the 25 to 29 and 30 to 34 year-old brackets, twice as high, or even higher, than the opium users or the Tai Lam addicts at large. On the other hand, regarding those still clinging to opium, 44 per cent were in the 55 years or more age bracket, as compared in the same age group with only 7 per cent heroin users and a 23 per cent general Tai Lam population (which, as we have seen, has an unusually large share of old men).

TABLE XXXI

LENGTH OF ADDICTION OF ADDICTS WHO USED EITHER HEROIN OR OPIUM, AS COM-
PARED WITH THE ENTIRE ADDICT GROUP AT TAI LAM PRISON

Length of Addiction	Heroin Only		Opium Only		Entire Study Group*	
	No. of Prisoners	%	No. of Prisoners	%	No. of Prisoners	%
5 years or less .	64	46	12	27.5	94	19
6—10 years . .	63	45	5	11.0	132	27
11—15 years .	11	8	7	16.0	99	20
16 years or more	2	1	20	45.5	161	34
Total	140	100	44	100.0	486	100

* From Table VIII, p. 56.

Table XXXI shows the length of addiction of the same three groups. Ninety-one per cent of the heroin users — most of whom, as we have seen, were in the younger age groups, — also had a relatively short length of addiction — ten years or less. No doubt, most of them were introduced to narcotics at the time heroin had begun to replace opium.

Among the opium-only users, it is not surprising to find a high figure for the group addicted 16 years or more, since many of these addicts were old men. Because of the small figures for the opium users, a more detailed interpretation cannot be undertaken, but a breakdown (Table XXXII) of those whose length of addiction is 16 years or more shows that 70 per cent (14) had used opium for 30 years or more (Table XXXII), with the maximum length being 50 years.

TABLE XXXII

LENGTH OF ADDICTION OF OPIUM-ONLY USERS AT TAI LAM
(Detailed Breakdown of Those Whose Length of Addiction is 16 Years or More)

16 years	1
20 years	1
21 years	1
24 years	1
26 years	2
30 years	7
32 years	1
35 years	1
40 years	2
41 years	1
42 years	1
50 years	1
Total	20

In addition to noting those who used only one drug, Tai Lam work books sometimes also noted reasons given by addicts as to why they had changed from opium to heroin. Thus, numbers 3361 to 3560 (i.e., 200 prisoners) stated they had made the change because heroin was cheaper.

To see if the figures support the reason given for the change in drug used, let us compare the daily amount spent by those who took either heroin or opium exclusively. According to Table XXXIII, (A.), the heroin users do not spend less on their drug than the opium users, but even slightly more (5 per cent). The difference becomes more evident when one deducts those few persons (B.) who spent unusually high amounts, that is, over H. K. $ 25 per day (7 per cent).[80]

TABLE XXXIII

MEAN AMOUNT SPENT ON DRUGS DAILY BY TAI LAM ADDICTS USING ONE DRUG
EXCLUSIVELY

	Amount Spent (H.K. Dollars)	
	Heroin Only	Opium Only
A. All One-Drug Users	7.63	7.39
B. One-Drug Users Spending $ 25 or less .	7.34	6.84

Addicts Who Administer Drugs Intravenously

Since American drug users today commonly use an injection to administer heroin to themselves, I thought it might be interesting to study those addicts in Hong Kong who also used this method. As pointed out earlier in this Chapter, most Hong Kong addicts generally take heroin by such famous methods of inhalation as the ones called "Chasing the Dragon" and "Firing the Anti-Aircraft Gun." Intravenous injection of heroin is very seldom used by Hong Kong addicts. Only seven cases out of our sample of 500 were found — too few for a special investigation. In the records for the entire 5 000 addicts at Tai Lam, however, 51 cases were found in which addicts had used the injection method.[81] Although 51 is still a small figure, a few details will be presented about this group.

The average daily amount spent by these addicts was H. K. $ 8.70. From the meager records in the Tai Lam books, it was not always clear what drug the addict had used in the past. Nevertheless, this much can be said. Of the 51 addicts taking narcotics intravenously, 19 had a history of addiction to both heroin and opium, 25 (50 per cent) had no known addiction to opium, and 7 had no known addiction to heroin. This last figure is, of course, confusing. If they were not addicted to heroin, what, then, did they inject? Was it perhaps morphine?

Table XXXIV shows the occupations of these addicts.[82] Interestingly enough, a relatively high percentage of seamen are found in this group,

TABLE XXXIV

OCCUPATIONS OF TAI LAM ADDICTS WHO USED INTRAVENOUS INJECTIONS *

Occupation	Tai Lam Addicts	
	Number	%
Unemployed	1	2
Street Occupations	6	12
Unskilled	22	43
Skilled	16	31
Commercial and Professional	1	2
Fishermen and Farmers	1	2
Seamen	4	8
Total	51	100

* This and the following tables concerning users of intravenous injections are compiled from the entire work books.

indicating a possibility that they might have learned the injection method through their contact with addicts in other countries. Otherwise, the distribution of occupations is not too different from that of the other addict groups investigated.

TABLE XXXV

REASONS FOR DRUG USE GIVEN BY TAI LAM ADDICTS USING INTRAVENOUS INJECTIONS

Reason	Addicts at Tai Lam	
	Number	%
Medical	39	78
Nonmedical	11	22
Total	50	100

For those using the injection method, the percentage of cases in which medical reasons were given is much higher than for our "regular" addict population at Tai Lam (Table XXXV).[83]

The age distribution in Table XXXVI shows that a large number of those using intravenous injections are in the 41-to-45 year old age bracket.

TABLE XXXVI

AGE DISTRIBUTION OF TAI LAM ADDICTS USING INTRAVENOUS INJECTIONS

Age Group	Addicts at Tai Lam	
	Number	%
25 years or less	2	4.0
26—30 years	3	6.0
31—35 years	8	16.5
36—40 years	9	18.5
41—45 years	11	22.5
46—50 years	4	8.0
51—55 years	7	14.5
56 years or more	5	10.0
Total	49	100.0

Juveniles

Hong Kong authorities stress that the number of juvenile drug users in the Colony is small.[84] To get an idea of just how small, we shall use figures taken from the annual reports of the Hong Kong courts and probation services. During the year ending March 31, 1961, 10 narcotics offenders up to fifteen years of age were placed on probation; of these, 4 were girls under fourteen.[85] That same year, 38 social investigations were made of minors under twenty-one years of age who had committed drug offenses; 3 of these were for girls under fourteen.[86] Table XXXVII shows the small number of juveniles sentenced for narcotics offenses by the magistrate courts from 1955/56 to 1960/61. These figures do not distinguish between juvenile drug users and those children who may have been caught peddling and transporting narcotics, the number of convicted children who are actually addicted is extremely insignificant.[87] Because of the few juveniles convicted as well as the legal changes that have occurred, no further interpretation of this Table can be made with respect to a trend in juvenile drug addiction.

TABLE XXXVII

JUVENILES CONVICTED FOR NARCOTICS OFFENSES BY HONG KONG MAGISTRATES COURTS, 1955—1961 *

| Years | Sentence | | Total |
	Imprisonment	Fine	
1955—56	9 a	4	13
1956—57	25 b	2	27
1957—58	4	1	5
1958—59	9 c	1	10
1959—60	7 d	—	7
1960—61	1	—	1

* Registrar, Supreme Court, *Annual Departmental Reports*. These figures are for both girls and boys. Those receiving first offender treatment or a warning are not included.
a Includes four who were whipped.
b Includes eight who were whipped.
c Includes three who were whipped.
d Includes one who was whipped.

Juveniles, it seems, are used relatively frequently to transport or peddle narcotics, since they are less likely to be suspected than adults. During both my stays the Hong Kong press carried stories about such abuses. For example, the *Hong Kong Tiger Standard*[88] carried the story of an American sailor who was being tried in the South Kowloon Magistracy after having purchased heroin from a child. Another case involved a drug ring of twelve adults and two juveniles. [89]

It is believed that shoeshine boys, reportedly controlled by Triad societies [90] also participate in trafficking. One Hong Kong drug specialist even believed that these shoeshine boys were responsible for most of the juvenile drug consumption being committed in the Colony.

Social workers in the Colony told me they found that young persons in Hong Kong sometimes take up the trafficking of narcotic drugs merely to have a job.

Considering the fact that children in such an overcrowded place as Hong Kong are often exposed to narcotics, [91] it is indeed amazing that so few do get into trouble for narcotics offenses.

Although the broader problem of juvenile delinquency in general lies outside the scope of this report, it is noteworthy that in Hong Kong the small number of juvenile drug users who come to the attention of the authorities parallels the low number of juvenile delinquents there. As Table XXXVIII indicates, the number of juveniles "punished" by the courts is about one-thirteenth the number of adults who are punished. [92] During 1960/61, only 82 persons fifteen years old or less were committed by the courts to institutions after a social investigation had been made. [93] Even if one assumes that a large number of juveniles who do not come to the attention of the courts, might be in the "punishable behaviour"

TABLE XXXVIII

NUMBER OF JUVENILES AND ADULTS PUNISHED BY THE HONG KONG MAGISTRATES COURTS IN 1960/61 *

Population		No. of Persons Punished	Rate of Persons Punished per 10 000 Inhabitants
Juveniles	633 703 a	2 898	46
Adults	1 812 649 b	110 979	612

* Compiled from the *Annual Departmental Report* 1960—61, Table X, pp. 23—27 and from the 1961 *Census*, Vol. 2, Tables 103 and 109, pp. 18—24.

a Total population 7 to 15 years of age.

b Total population 16 years old or more.

category, juvenile delinquency would still not constitute a pressing problem in the Colony. The phenomenon of low delinquency rates is also found among Chinese-Americans in the United States. [94]

Women

As Tables V and VI on pp. 52, 53 show, the number of women convicted for narcotics offenses by Hong Kong magistrates from 1955/56 to 1960/61 is very small in comparison to the number of men convicted (approximately 3 per cent women to 97 per cent men). Yet, Hong Kong's total population is nearly equally divided, 49 per cent of the population are women and 51 per cent men. [95]

From data obtained by the courtesy of the Prison Administration concerning addicted inmates at Lai Chi Kok Prison (where all female offenders in the Colony are sent) a limited insight into drug use among Hong Kong women may be gained. [96] Out of a total number of 362 women admitted to the prison from January to June 1961, 192 had been committed for dangerous drug offenses. Of 135 "confessed addicts", 15 used opium, 120 used heroin, and none used morphine. To state it another way, only one-ninth used opium, the others used heroin. A Hong Kong woman consuming heroin by "chasing the dragon", is shown in Illustration 10.

TABLE XXXIX

MPARISON OF AGE DISTRIBUTION FOR THE GENERAL FEMALE POPULATION AND WOMEN ADDICTS
AT LAI CHI KOK PRISON*

Age Group	General Female Population		Female Addict Prisoners							
			First Half of 1961				1960			
	Number	%	Opium	Heroin	Total	%	Opium	Heroin	Total	%
—34	330 515	40	3	42	45	33	4	129	133	33
—50	304 016	36	11	71	82	61	17	208	225	57
—65	144 260	17	1	7	8	6	5	30	35	9
or more	55 201	7	—	—	—	—	—	4	4	1
tal	833 992	100	15	120	135	100	26	371	397	100

* Population figures from *1961 Census*, Tables 103 and 109, pp. 18, 24.

Table XXXIX compares the age distribution of Hong Kong's female population with the age distribution of women addict prisoners at Lai Chi Kok during 1960 and 1961. The number of addict prisoners 35 to 50 years old is about 60 per cent higher than the number of women the same age in the general population; while the number of addict prisoners 20 to 34 years old is 18 per cent lower.

Illustration 10.
WOMAN SMOKING HEROIN BY "CHASING THE DRAGON"

(Photo H.K. Police Narcotics Bureau, 1959;
Courtesy H.K. Government Information Services)

The breakdown of occupations of the female addict prisoners (Table XL) reveals that one-fourth of them are prostitutes. Taken together, the number of unemployed addicts and addicts of low-status occupations (street occupations, unskilled laborers, and prostitutes) constitute about 80 per cent to 90 per cent of the total. Interestingly, a relatively high percentage of women were employed in commerce and the professions (7.5 per cent and 6 per cent as compared with 1.6 per cent and 3 per cent for the men). Do perhaps nurses account for this high percentage?

TABLE XL

OCCUPATIONS OF WOMEN ADDICTS AT LAI CHI KOK PRISON

Occupation	Addict Prisoners							
	January—June, 1961				1960			
	Opium	Heroin	Total		Opium	Heroin	Total	
			No.	%			No.	%
...employed	4	38	42	31.0	5	140	145	36.5
...eet Occupations	2	5	7	5.5	2	21	23	6.0
...skilled Laborers	1	22	23	17.0	11	70	81	20.5
...lled Workers	—	—	—	—	—	—	—	—
...mmerce and Professions	—	10	10	7.5	—	24	24	6.0
...hermen and Farmers	—	—	—	—	—	2	2	0.5
...stitutes	1	37	38	28.0	3	97	100	25.0
...usewives	7	8	15	11.0	5	17	22	5.5
...tals	15	120	135	100.0	26	371	397	100.0

The reader should be reminded that statistical figures from the Colony do not always distinguish between users and traffickers. Narcotics use among women may be relatively rare, but women as well as children frequently engage in trafficking since law enforcement personnel, mostly male, cannot easily search them. I understand that most of the female pushers come primarily from those occupational groups (prostitutes, hawkers, and dance-hall girls) to which the Triad societies reportedly pay particular attention.[97]

[1] *1959 White Paper*, para. 22.
[2] "Language snag in court case" in *Hong Kong Tiger Standard*, Sept. 21, 1963.
[3] *1959 White Paper*, para. 6.
[4] According to officials.
[5] Directly or indirectly via Malaya, Singapore, or ports on the island of Borneo. Since 1959, the Hong Kong authorities became also aware of narcotics that had been air-dropped by pilots from Laos in the Gulf of Siam/South China

area, and that were being smuggled into the Colony. See *Illicit Traffic: Hong Kong*, p. 5.

6 *Illicit Traffic: Hong Kong*, pp. 6 ff.

7 *1959 White Paper*, para. 21.

8 *Illicit Traffic in Hong Kong*, p. 8.

9 "We have no land frontier problems in relation to illicit traffic." *Ibid.*, p. 1.

10 *Ibid.*, para. 5 — see also the illustration facing p. 9 of that publication.

11 *Hong Kong Tiger Standard*, October 31, 1961.

12 *Illicit Traffic: Hong Kong*, p. 7.

13 *Ibid.*

14 *Bangkok World*, October 4, 1961.

15 *Ibid.*, October 7, 1961.

16 *Illicit Traffic in Hong Kong*, p. 8.

17 *1959 White Paper*, para. 3.

18 Way, E. Leong, "Control and Treatment of Drug Addiction in Hong Kong". Paper presented at the Narcotics Conference held at the University of California at Los Angeles, April 27—28 1963.

19 *1959 White Paper*, para. 9.

20 K.S.C. Pillai, "The Puff of Ruin", *Far Eastern Economic Review*, Vol. 41, no. 12, pp. 759—764 ("one in every 12 of the 3.6 million people in Hong Kong is an addict"; p. 761). Elsewhere, the author states that "one-third of the male population over 15 in the lower income group are drug addicts." (p. 763).

21 In an undated appeal for financial support.

22 Hong Kong Narcotics Advisory Committee, *Progress Report 1959/60*, para. 4.

23 *Ibid.*

24 *Ibid.*, Appendix I(a), p. 18.

25 United Nations, *Incidence of Drug Addiction* (1963; U.N. Document No. E/CN.7/439), p. 10.

26 Hong Kong Commissioner of Police, *Annual Departmental Report 1960/61*, para. 150.

27 Roughly 30 to 80 times as potent as opium *(1959 White Paper*, para. 3).

28 According to the press, when, in September 1963, a factory was discovered in a pig sty on Lumma Island, a witness stated: "Sometimes, at night, there was a smell like fish coming from the pig sty, but I minded my own business." *South China Morning Post*, Sept. 24, 1963.

29 See below Table **XXXIV**.

30 *1959 White Paper*, para. 4.

31 *Ibid.*, para. 15. Sometimes the underworld will provide guards who watch out for approaching police.

32 *Hong Kong Tiger Standard,* October 15 and 16, 1961.

33 For a picture of such a divan, see *1959 White Paper*, fourth illustration between pp. 4 and 5.

34 United Nations. Commission on Narcotics Drugs. *The Illicit Traffic in Narcotic Drugs in Sout-East Asia.* (1963, U.N. Document No. E/CN.7/440). Malaya and Singapore now form part of Malaysia. An airborne international operation is described in *Revue internationale de Police criminelle*, Vol. 17, No. 162, Nov. 1962, p. 287. For a colorful description of such an operation,

see also S. Karnow, "The Opium Must Go Through", in *Life*, Vol. 55, No. 9, Aug. 30, 1963, pp. 11—12.

35 This description is based mainly on W. P. Morgan's *Triad Societies in Hong Kong* (Hong Kong, Government Press, 1960).

36 *Ibid.*, p. 89. Morgan remarks: "Not an impressive amount compared to some of the American crime syndicates, but quite considerable enough in a Colony as small as Hong Kong."

37 *Ibid.*, p. IX.

38 *Ibid.*, p. 89.

39 Para. 182.

40 *Ibid.* See also W. P. Morgan, "The Work of the Police Force in Hong Kong", *Corona*, Vol. 14, No. 9, Sept. 1962, pp. 329—333 (especially, p. 332).

41 Commissioner of Police, *Annual Report 1961—62*, Appendix VII, Table F, p. 63.

42 *Ibid.*, paras. 24, 134—136.

43 "Deportees in Trouble Again", *Hong Kong Tiger Standard* of Sept. 19, 1963, and other press articles in that journal and in the *South China Morning Post* from Sept. 19 to Oct. 10, 1963.

44 *South China Morning Post*, Sept. 21, 1963, p. 8; Sept. 27, 1963, p. 8; Sept. 28, 1963, p. 8.

45 As far as I could make out, the unavailability of these records introduced no statistical bias into this material.

46 That is, as far as the documentation I used is concerned. Most or all of these data are no doubt available elsewhere. I understand that previous convictions are part of the individual's general prison record where they are clipped together and often present a clear picture of the general penal "career".

47 According to the *1959 White Paper,* data on the addict prisoners at Tai Lam constituted "at least one important and reliable source of information" on Hong Kong addicts in general (para. 8). While all Tai Lam prisoners had also been at one time at Victoria, the central classification and reception prison of Hong Kong, there is no danger that the same addict may have been counted twice and appears in both the prison populations which form the subject of this statistical investigation. The date of the sample week of intake at Victoria falls *after* the last date of intake in the Tai Lam group.

48 Hong Kong Census Commissioner (K. M. A. Barnett), *Hong Kong Report on the 1961 Census.* (Hong Kong, Government Press, c. 1962), 3 vols. (referred to in this study as the *1961 Census).*

49 To appreciate this, we should also remember that in the United States the proportion of male to female drug users is approximately 5 : 1.

50 Under the Juvenile Offenders Ordinance, a person under the age of 14 is still considered a "child", at 14 and 15 he is considered a "young person". Thus, a person who is 16 years old or more will fall under adult criminal jurisdiction. However, since very few teen-agers in Hong Kong are addicts, we have used 20 years as the lower age limit, a figure more suitable for comparison.

51 Cases of unknown age are omitted. Similarly, the number of unknown cases for variables shown in the other tables are also not given.

52 Addicts to other drugs, though occasionally found in Hong Kong, were not

found in any of the two groups.

53 The reader may note that we use two different age groupings. On table IX and some of the other tables following, the age brackets for each five-year group are written as 26—30, 31—35, and so forth, as opposed to the style of grouping used in the other tables (25—29, 30—34, etc.). When, after preparing most of the tables, the figures of the *1961 Census* (which uses the latter style of age grouping) became available to me, I had to change the groupings on those tables where comparisons were made with the Hong Kong population at large. However, it seemed unnecessary to me to rearrange all tables.

54 As I have already pointed out, my policy in rounding out figures was to avoid exaggerating the length of addiction. Similarly, I did not wish to make the addiction age appear younger than it actually is. Therefore, partial years (such as 23½ years) were counted as full years (24 years), in calculating the addiction age.

55 "Remarks by Mayor Robert F. Wagner at the White House Conference on Narcotics," Press Release, September 27, 1962, p. 3.

56 On tolerance and its implications see: United States. The White House *Ad Hoc* Panel on Drug Abuse. *Progress Report, 1962,* pp. 16—17.

57 *Ibid.,* p. 39.

58 *1959 White Paper,* Table I (b), p. 17.

59 So much can be said that the 34 681 male professionals of Hong Kong, — forming 4.6 of the male working population 18 and over, — are no doubt much underrepresented, considering that the *combined* "Commerce and Professions" group amounts to much less in both Tai Lam and Victoria. See *1961 Census,* Vol. 3, Table 226, p. 17.

60 *1959 White Paper,* para. 10.

61 *Ibid.,* para. 10.

62 See *1961 Census,* Vol. II, Table 109, p. 24, and Vol. III, Table 311, p. 47.

63 Because of the sparse figures on the unemployed addicts (especially at Victoria with only four cases), not much weight should be given to the proportions of unemployment among the addicts to those of the population.

64 Certain of the records contained such notations as "completed middle school." With the help of persons familiar with school systems in Hong Kong and China, these have been translated as best as possible into years of education. In calculating the average, the group listed in Table XXVII as "9 years and over" was estimated as 10 years, since the exact length of studies for addicts who had attended higher academic institutions was not always given.

65 Elsewhere, the *1961 Census* states that 90.72 per cent of the male population 10 years old or more were able to read and write Chinese, English, or some other language. Incidentally, the literacy rate for females in the Colony, though it has risen considerably, is only 57.55 per cent according to the *1961 Census,* Vol. I, Table 158, p. 69.

66 Nevertheless, among the general Hong Kong population there are nearly 100 000 bosses or "permanent monthly-paid" employees who have had no schooling whatsoever. Commenting on this the *1961 Census* stated that, in the Colony, nothing "succeeds like success." (Vol. 3, sec. 21.2.9.3, p. CXIV)

This maxim, however, may not necessarily apply to opiate users.

[67] As far as fishermen are concerned, this is not surprising. In the Colony 30 078 of 35 312 male and female fisherfolk 14 years old and up (87 per cent) were found to have had no schooling. (*1961 Census;* Vol. 3, p. 71, Table 420.)

[68] Calculated from *1961 Census,* Vol. 3, Table 225, p. 16.

[69] The medical reasons are, to be sure, expressed in lay terms and not always clearly. Thus Table XX which was compiled from these statements, should be regarded with some reservation.

[70] Figure obtained by courtesy of the Prison Administration.

[71] A number of legal changes took place during the period studied, most of them concerned the questions of whether certain drugs (such as barbiturates) should be regarded as dangerous and also the severity of penalties imposed. No consideration could be given to these changes in this study of offenses.

[72] *1959 White Paper,* para. 6. The amendments of 1960 have done away with the distinction between heroin and other drug offenses, although judicial practice may still make this distinction.

[73] *Ibid.,* para. 13.

[74] From the amendment to the Dangerous Drugs Regulations, *Government Gazette,* No. 56, Suppl. 2, Nov. 18, 1960.

[75] Revised edition of 1950, with numerous subsequent amendments.

[76] *1959 White Paper,* para. 16.

[77] Ibid.

[78] *Hong Kong Tiger Standard,* October 25, 1961.

[79] The lower age limits are not the same for the two columns in Table XXVIII. As, however, there are no more suitable figures available, the small difference may be left out of consideration.

[80] There are 2 such cases among the heroin-only addicts and 1 among the opium-only addicts.

[81] This figure includes the 7 addicts in the sample of 500 who used this method.

[82] Compare these figures with Table XV on p. 62 of this chapter.

[83] Compare with Table XX, on p. 67 of this chapter.

[84] *Progress Report 1959—1960,* para. 4.

[85] Director of Social Welfare, *Annual Departmental Report 1960—1961,* Appendix 11, p. 41.

[86] *Ibid.,* Appendix 12, p. 43.

[87] Compare these figures with Tables II and III on pp. 39 and 40 of this chapter. To my knowledge, no annual figures are available on the juvenile population for the years preceding the *1961 Census,* so that "rates" cannot be established.

[88] October 25, 1961.

[89] *Hong Kong Tiger Standard,* October 6, 1963.

[90] Morgan, *op. cit.,* p. 89.

[91] See, for example, Illustration 8 on page 46, presumably a photograph of an actual narcotics divan in which in small boy can be seen in the right-hand corner.

[92] Both "children" under the age of fourteen and "young persons" of fourteen

and fifteen fall under the jurisdiction of the Juvenile Offenders Ordinance (Chapter 226).

93 Director of Social Welfare, *Annual Departmental Report 1960/61,* Appendix 12B, p. 44. Although no figures are available as to whether any juveniles were committed for addiction *without* being investigated, they most likely were not since the number of commitments to training centers on this chart is practically the same (122) as the number compiled from the statistics on dispositions by the five Hong Kong Magistracies (Registrar, Supreme Court, *Annual Departmental Report, 1960/61,* Table IX, pp. 18—22).

94 Stuart H. Cattell, *Health, Welfare and Social Organization in Chinatown, New York City* (New York Community Service Society, 1962), p. 61 ff. The author, however, has a pessimistic outlook on the future trend of delinquency among Chinese-American youngsters of the third generation in New York.

95 See Tables V and VI on pp. 52 and 53 of this chapter.

96 These data were used, as they were available. The breakdown is different from the data given earlier in this chapter for male addict prisoners.

97 A survey, undertaken in 1955, of 260 Hong Kong prostitutes found not one of them taking drugs. Fu Shang-Ling, *Statistical Report on the Sample Survey of Prostitutes in Hong Kong.* Submitted to the Sub-Committee of Moral Welfare, Social Welfare Advisory Committee, Social Welfare Department, Government of Hong Kong. (Hong Kong, n.p., c.1955), p. 12.

CHAPTER IV

PREVENTIVE MEASURES IN HONG KONG

In considering Hong Kong's preventive measures against narcotics addiction, the reader should bear in mind the general socio-economic situation in the Colony — its population explosion, its extreme housing shortage, its peculiar position as a large free port, its growing industrialization and concomitant labor problems. Beyond this, the reader will also remember that Hong Kong's population is 98 per cent Chinese and that the Chinese tradition, as it has developed during China's long history, has its own well-tried remedies for social problems. Such a strong tradition does not always look favorably at the introduction of new measures.

General Social Services

A number of social measures have been undertaken in Hong Kong which are not directly aimed at the drug addict, but which, as a by-product, may be of some benefit for the prevention of drug use through the general improvements which they promote. These undertakings merit the greatest praise in light of their own goals; an evaluation of their success from the specific angle of their preventing drug addiction is not possible at this time.

Resettlement

In a city filled with squatters, roof-top dwellers and street sleepers, the resettlement of persons living in such abnormal conditions is one of the major tasks of the Colony. The first steps towards such a resettlement were taken in 1948.

In earlier years, sub-standard dwellers were placed in housing in the form of cottages, but this was found unsatisfactory.[1] Around 1954 the

construction of low cost "multi-storey resettlement blocks" forming
so-called "estates" began.[2] The program is under the supervision of the
Government's Resettlement Department, with the semi-official Housing
Authority and the Hong Kong Housing Society participating. By the end
of the year 1961-62, over 460 000 persons had been resettled.[3] In addition, many other housing projects are privately sponsored, often with
the encouragement and financial support of the Government.

The speed with which these settlements are being built is impressive;
every ninth day a new block is complete.[4] By the end of March 1962,
there were 179 resettlement blocks of six and seven stories available.
The average room has a floor space of 120 square feet and is destined to
accommodate a family of four or five adults. A child under 10 is counted
as half an adult. The rent for such a room is H.K. $ 14 per month. To
get an idea of these apartments, 120 square feet, the area allotted to five
adults, is the size of an average rug 10 x 12 feet (3 x 3.60 meters)
frequently found in Western homes. In the older estates all the rooms
were this size. In the newer ones there is some flexibility; rooms vary
from 86 square feet for 3 to 3-$1/3$ adults at $ 10, up to 240 square feet
for families of 8 to 10 adults, or for sharing by two smaller families, at
$ 28.

Conceivably, these accomplishments in the field of resettlement may
help to improve the narcotics situation in the Colony. Resettlement may
be beneficial to the settlers' health, so that less resort to narcotics may
be sought as a cure. Also, better housing may reduce the nervous strain
on the resettled persons, and, if it is true that low resistance to strain
plays a role in causing a person's addiction, such a reduction of strain
may be beneficial. No evaluation studies exist as yet.

During the year 1961—62, 13 resettled tenancies were terminated out
of a total of 254 terminations for trafficking of heroin; possibly there
were also other drug offenses among the 39 terminations for miscellaneous
reasons.[4a] When, in October 1963, a complaint was lodged against heroin
addiction and peddling at the Shekkipmei Estate, the reply was made
that the number of prosecutions for drug offenses committed at that
Estate had been low.[4b] Here, as almost everywhere in the field of drug
offenses it is not known how much narcotics activity may be going on
which does not come to the attention of the police. The "tenancy card"

in resettlement projects contains a clause forbidding illegal activities in the rooms. [4c] Thus, the use or the sale of narcotics becomes a reason for immediate termination of the tenant's contract. As we shall see, this plays an important part in the deliberations of Tai Lam Prison's Board of Aftercare.

The public health measures are another form of social service which may be helpful in preventing narcotics addiction. In contrast to other Asian countries, the general health of the Colony may be quite good in spite of occasional epidemics and despite such problems as continuing population expansion, overcrowding, lack of adequate housing, and restricted water supply. Yet, as we have seen, narcotics addicts are not always part of this good health picture; indeed, 55 per cent to 61 per cent of them, if we remember, had given medical reasons for their addiction. [5] At Tai Lam, as we shall see, about 40 per cent of the population is on sick call every day. Thirteen per cent of the prison population (that is, 100 out of 700) were under treatment for *open* tuberculosis, [5a] while in the general adult population, only an estimated 2 to 3 per cent had this disease in an active form. [6] As mentioned before, Chinese in poor health often do not visit a physician. Such a "modern" way of dealing with illness may still be foreign to many among the Chinese population who are not yet ready to give up their traditional ways. At any rate, the services of a Western-style doctor, are also far beyond their financial means.

I was told that, when sick, many Chinese will first visit a *Chung-i*, a Chinese herb doctor. If this does not help and if the illness begins to interfere with his work, he may become afraid of losing his job. At this point he often turns to self-medication through opium or heroin.

In view of the apparently close relationship, already mentioned between general physical health and the use of narcotics in Hong Kong, the overall expansion of health services may also help in the prevention of addiction. Hospital beds are scarce in Hong Kong, but both the Government and nongovernmental agencies are establishing easily accessible out-patient medical centers. Among the private organizations which helped to set up out-patient clinics were the Royal Hong Kong Jockey Club, the Lutheran World Federation, [7] and many others, especially many of the Hong Kong Chinese voluntary and charitable organizations. [7a]

At the end of 1961, there were sixty-two such clinics treating 5 600 000 persons.[7b]

With the establishment of these clinics their popularity increases, and Hong Kong authorities consider the growing demand for "Western-style" medical treatment a hopeful sign.[8] From 1954 to 1961, for example, the attendance at Government out-patient centers had increased by 132 per cent.[8a] It is hoped that the wider use of these medical facilities may help to reduce the do-it-yourself curing of ailments by means of opium or heroin.

Law Enforcement

In Hong Kong, as in other places, law enforcement plays an indispensable part in the prevention of narcotics addiction. Unlike other countries, however, Hong Kong has its own peculiar problems. One of them is that it is a free port, whose trading activities cannot be greatly interfered with or hampered. Other problems of law enforcement are the Colony's rugged shore line and terrain, its overcrowded cities, the housing shortage, and the tremendous refugee problem. Still another peculiar feature of the Colony may be the fact that a large number of Hong Kong inhabitants reportedly are members of triad societies, although the significance of these societies seems to be decreasing. Hong Kong also has a problem of corruption among the lower grades of civil servants. Although this particular problem may not, to be sure, be as prevalent or as widespread as in some other countries, it is nevertheless important enough to justify the following statement made recently by two government committees:

> "We have absolutely no doubt from the evidence and statistics we have studied that corruption exists on a scale which justifies the strongest countermeasures."[9]

Of all the complaints about corruption which these two committees received, about half concerned the police force.[10] Drug trafficking may also play a part in this corruption.

In actuality, however, the enforcement of narcotics law has been very efficient — an observation shown not only by spectacular seizures of contraband drugs but also by a generally rising trend in the price of narcotics. Table XLI shows the average daily amount spent by Tai Lam and Victoria addicts for their drug supply, according to the reports made by several groups of prisoners at different times since 1959. The Tai Lam prisoners are assigned consecutive numbers on entering the institution, thus the numbers in the Table indicate the chronological order of their entry; the Victoria inmates constitute the latest group.

TABLE XLI

AVERAGE DAILY AMOUNT SPENT BY VARIOUS GROUPS OF TAI LAM AND VICTORIA PRISONERS ON DRUGS, 1959—1961

	Average Daily Amount Spent *
Tai Lam Prisoner's, Nos. 1350—1551 . . .	3.97
Tai Lam Prisoner's, Nos. 2350—2550 . . .	3.40
Tai Lam Prisoner's, Nos. 3350—3550 . . .	3.59
Tai Lam Prisoner's, Nos. 4350—4550 . . .	4.81
Tai Lam Prisoner's, Nos. 5350—5550 . . .	7.11
Tai Lam Group studied in this report Nos. 6025—6526.	7.72
Victoria Addicts	7.73

* In Hong Kong dollars.

As can be seen, the daily amount spent by the addicts, after an initial decline from H.K. $ 3.97 to H.K. $ 3.40, has risen to H.K. $ 7.72. Contributing to this rise, which began early in 1960, with the group numbered 3350—3550 may have been the Government's anti-narcotics drive of that year. [11]

Law enforcement in Hong Kong is mainly in the hands of two Government agencies, the Preventive Service and the Police which are next described.

Preventive Service

The Preventive Service is part of the Department of Commerce and Industry. It has a special Narcotics Section which, in cooperation with the Narcotics Bureau of the Police, is responsible for the prevention of narcotics smuggling into and out of the Colony. The members of the Preventive Service wear a police-like uniform, and, as to their discipline and morale, were judged "satisfactory" in the Department's *Annual*

Report.[12] During 1950 to 1960, the manpower of this Narcotics Section was increased eightfold,[13] so that by March 31, 1961, its staff comprised 552 men.[14]

During 1962, the Service guarded 539 ships which had arrived in the port of Hong Kong from "narcotics ports" (i.e., ports from which smuggling of drugs might be expected) and 4 505 ocean-going vessels; it inspected 1 292 aircraft, and searched 22 047 native vessels. It also made daily searches of the passenger ferries operating between Hong Kong and Macau. During that same period, the Service made 36 major seizures of drugs and accompanying paraphernalia, the largest of which, found inside a cargo of teak boards, yielded 768 pounds of raw opium, 16 pounds of prepared opium, 45½ pounds of morphine, and 293½ pounds of morphine-hydrochloride.[15]

Police

While the Preventive Service deals principally with illegal traffic into and out of Hong Kong, the police were concerned mainly with the unlawful manufacture, traffic, and consumption of narcotics within the Colony (although it does have numerous international connections through its membership in the International Criminal Police Organization — INTERPOL, and through direct connection with other countries).

Drug problems are handled by the Narcotics Bureau, which is headed by a senior superintendent of police.[16] In addition to its close cooperation with the Preventive Service and foreign police forces, the Bureau's functions include "the prevention and detection of narcotic offenses, the collection and collation of narcotic intelligence and the investigation of narcotic offenses."[17] Within the General Investigation Section of the Hong Kong Police, an anti-narcotics squad composed of specialists was established in the fiscal year of 1960/61. This squad operates independently but in cooperation with Anti-Narcotics Bureau units.[18] In addition, the Hong Kong and Kowloon districts of the Police also formed one special squad each during 1961/62.[18a]

Policewomen are used effectively in dangerous drug raids; and two police dogs are specially trained to detect and locate these drugs.[18b]

In 1960/61, under the chairmanship of the Deputy Commissioner of

Police, a Force Narcotics Committee was also appointed "to coordinate all police action against drug addiction and trafficking."[19] Seizures made by both the police and the Preventive Service have already been listed in Chapter III.[20]

Courts

Since the Magistrates Courts of Hong Kong handle the bulk of narcotics offenders, I attended a session in the Kowloon magistracy in one of the older courthouses of the Colony. Here, the Judge or Magistrate sits alone in court and a uniformed police inspector acts as prosecutor. The official language of the court is English, so that the entire trial usually has to be interpreted into that language by several court interpreters speaking the different Chinese dialects. Cantonese is by far the most popular dialect. Since everyone — the magistrate, the prosecutor, the interpreters, and the defendants — usually speaks Cantonese, the English translation is occasionally handled rather summarily, sometimes making it hard for a foreigner without a knowledge of that dialect to follow the court procedure.

The morning I attended, all thirty cases tried were petty cases of larceny, prostitution, drug offenses, and so on, in which the defendants had already admitted their guilt and in which only a few minutes were given to each case. An unusual sight for me was the tremendous defendants' cage, three to four yards deep and taking up nearly the full width of the large courtroom. Situated between the front section (holding the Judge's bench, the interpreters, and the prosecutor's table) and the rear seats (for visitors and persons awaiting trial), this cage held those who had been taken into custody. When his case came up, each defendant answered questions standing within this cage. Defendants who were not caged would, when called upon, step forward from the rear of the court and reply to the accusations and questions. This cage has been done away with in the new courthouses. During my 1963 stay, I visited Causeway Bay Magistracy where detained prisoners answer charges from a "dock". In that session, I did not see any lawyers in the courtroom acting as defense counsel for the accused.

No detailed statistics are available on the sentencing practices of the Hong Kong courts with respect to narcotics offenses. Some magistrates explained to me that a first offender who either possessed opium or attended a divan would usually be sentenced to a fine; while an offender who used heroin would usually receive a three-month prison sentence for a first offense, a six-month sentence for a second offense, up to a year for a third offense, and so on. If the quantity of narcotics found was so large that the accused appeared to be a peddler, more severe penalties were given.

Law

The main provisions on narcotics offenses are found either in the *Dangerous Drugs Ordinance* (Chapter 134) or in the *Dangerous Drugs Regulations.* Originally promulgated in 1935, both were amended a number of times until 1950 when a revised edition of both laws was issued. Since then, there has been a large number of further amendments, of which the most important are the first *Dangerous Drugs Amendment of Schedule Order, 1958* (which placed barbiturates under the provisions for dangerous drugs), the *Dangerous Drugs (Amendment) Ordinance, 1960,* the *Dangerous Drugs (Amendment) Regulations, 1961* (an amendment that did away with the distinction between opium and heroin offenses and imposed more severe maximum sentences), and the *Dangerous Drugs (Amendment) Ordinance, 1961,* (an amendment stipulating a maximum sentence of life imprisonment for manufacturing drugs).

Propaganda

One of the most important measures undertaken in Hong Kong was a propaganda campaign launched in November 1959 and coordinated by the Secretary for Chinese Affairs. Indeed, so important was the nature of this campaign, that an additional Assistant Secretary and a Narcotics Advisory Committee were appointed. All the members of this Committee belong to the Colony's Executive Council, the "Cabinet" of the Hong Kong Government.

The campaign was undertaken with considerable community support. Participating were the Kaifong neighborhood organizations, clansmen, adult education centers, the rural committees of the New Territories, and various clubs. By means of talks, broadcasts, press notices, leaflets, posters, and even an anti-narcotics concert and a Cantonese opera with a "strong anti-narcotics view," the campaign was put into operation. An anti-narcotics film in Cantonese dialect, entitled *The Hand of Death* and billed as a "Thriller" was shown in the local cinemas. [21]

Private organizations interested in the narcotics question carried on a propaganda campaign of their own through such media as competitions in anti-narcotics essay, poetry, play, song, and painting. [22]

Illustration 11.

POSTER USED DURING THE RECENT ANTI-NARCOTICS DRIVE

The object behind the addict is a Chinese coffin. The words read: "Addiction Means Death."

(Courtesy Hong Kong Secretary of Chinese Affairs)

The principal purposes of the campaign were to deter people from becoming users and to encourage addicts to seek a cure. Appendix A gives the texts of the leaflets issued, while Illustration 11 shows a poster (posters were also commonly used as the cover pictures of the leaflets) of an addict with a Chinese coffin in the background. The leaflet points out the evils which addiction creates, and exhorts the reader to cooperate with the Government and to avoid using narcotics. A second poster issued by the Government deals with divans, while a third shows the dangers of trafficking and pushing. In all three posters, the recurrent requests are (1) to avoid carrying packages for unknown people since, by doing so, the carrier may become a scapegoat for narcotic traffickers and (2) to furnish the Government authorities with any information on divans and particularly on illegal narcotics factories.

Each leaflet offers a reward for this type of information, and the rewards are to be bestowed by the higher police officers (whom the Government believes are better trusted by the population than are the lower-grade officers). During 1960/61, over 700 000 such leaflets and 40 000 posters were distributed. [23]

Interestingly, the Narcotics Advisory Committee came to the conclusion that there was a difference of opinion between the Government and the public at large regarding which aspect of the narcotics problem should receive priority publicity in the propaganda campaign. The public, it appeared, thought that the cure and rehabilitation of addicts should receive priority. The Government, on the other hand, while strongly interested in treatment of the addict, wanted its fight against smugglers and traffickers to receive priority. [24]

The propaganda drive by the Government against narcotics was still continuing, after approximately four years, during my second visit in 1963. At that time, for example, a Government spokesman reminded the public in a statement to the press that the Government had been offering rewards for information leading to the discovery of the drugs or arrest of traffickers. A detailed tariff was provided for these rewards, e.g., information on heroin carried an award of H.K. $ 20.— per ounce plus H.K. $ 10.— if there were an arrest and conviction. For quantities over four ounces, the reward climbed to H.K. $ 60.— per ounce plus H.K. $ 30.— for arrest and conviction. According to one of the newspapers, however, not many people in Hong Kong were aware of this offer.[24a]

Propaganda Campaign among Civil Servants

The Hong Kong Government paid particular attention to spreading propaganda among and through its civil servants. In 1960, the Secretary of Chinese Affairs requested all departmental heads to nominate a "departmental narcotics officer" whose main duties would include encouragement for all staff members to participate in the campaign, interdepartmental exchange of ideas and information, and creation and distribution of anti-narcotics publicity material. During October of that year, a special leaflet was printed in Chinese and distributed to over 50 000 government servants (Appendix B).[25]

Of all the departments participating in this campaign, the Police Department seems to have been one of the most active. Among other things, it organized a special exhibition at the police training school to apprise public leaders of the narcotics problem.[26]

Although no precise evaluation can be made in this report of the results of this campaign, my impression is that it greatly roused the interest and attention of the public.

The Government's request for information on the existence of divans and on the traffic and manufacture of narcotics has received a response described as "not surprisingly limited" and "lukewarm". The reasons given for these reactions were: (1), that the reputation of being known as an informer is not an especially savory one to have; (2), that informing took time and trouble, and (3), that many informers feared reprisals,[27] though such fears were unjustified.

Under these circumstances, the Government considers the campaign a success when "any member of the public other than the professional informers have supplied information to the Government Department on divans, etc."[28]

---

1 Hong Kong, Commissioner of Resettlement. *Annual Departmental Report 1961-62,* paras. 47—51.
2 *Ibid.,* paras. 52 ff.
3 *Ibid.,* para. 4.
4 Lutheran World Federation. *General Background Information on Hong Kong,*

Leaflet (Hong Kong, 1963), p. 2 (Hereafter cited as *Background*).

[4a] Hong Kong Commissioner of Resettlement, *op cit.*, para. 63.

[4b] *Hong Hong Tiger Standard,* October 2, 1963.

[4c] Hong Kong Commissioner of Resettlement, *op cit.*, para. 67.

[5] See Chapter III, Table XX, p. 67.

[5a] See Chapter V.

[6] *Hong Kong 1960,* p. 127; Lutheran World Federation, *op. cit.*, p. 2.

[7] Hong Kong Commissioner of Resettlement, *op. cit.*, p. 138—139; See also Lutheran World Federation, *Report,* 1963, p. 1.

[7a] Officials pointed out to me — as illustrative of a field in which Chinese and Western approaches are very similar — that the "properly run" clinics established and run by voluntary agencies exceed the Government ones both in numbers and in the number of patients they handle.

[7b] Lutheran World Service, *Background,* p. 5.

[8] *Hong Kong 1960,* p. 138.

[8a] Lutheran World Service, *Background,* p. 5.

[9] Standing Committee and Advisory Committee on Corruption, *Reports,* 1962, p. 40.

[10] *Ibid.,* p. 59.

[11] For further documentation on the rise of narcotics prices in Hong Kong, see also the United Nations Commission on Narcotics Drugs, *Report of the Sixteenth Session,* (April 24—May 10, 1961) para. 90 (U.N. Document E/3512—E/CN-7/411).

[12] Hong Kong Director of Commerce and Industry, *Annual Departmental Report 1960/61,* para. 58.

[13] Hong Kong Narcotics Advisory Committee, *Progress Report, November 1959 to October, 1960,* (By the Secretary for Chinese Affairs, Chairman) para. 11. In the following footnotes, this citation will be referred to as *Progress Report, 1959/60.*

[14] Hong Kong Director of Commerce and Industry, *op. cit.*, para. 56 and Table 14.

[15] Hong Kong Director of Commerce and Industry, *op. cit.*, paras. 279 ff. and, in particular, paras. 289 and 294. A detailed breakdown of seizures can be found in Table 12, p. 96.

[16] Until 1961/62, the Bureau was combined with the Anti-Corruptions Bureau (now a separate "Branch"). The Bureau of Narcotics has been integrated with the Criminal Investigation Department. Hong Kong Commissioner of Police, *Annual Report, 1961/62,* para. 48; *Ibid., 1960/61,* para. 185.

[17] *Ibid.,* 1960/61, para. 193.

[18] *Ibid.,* para. 174.

[18a] *Ibid.,* 1961/62, para. 139.

[18b] *Ibid.,* paras. 172, 174.

[19] *Ibid.,* 1960/61, para. 194.

[20] See Table I, p. 38 of Chapter III.

[21] *Progress Report 1959/60,* para. 32.

[22] *Ibid.,* para. 34.

[23] Hong Kong Secretary for Chinese Affairs, *Annual Departmental Report,*

1960/61, para. 20.

[24] *Progress Report, 1959/60,* para. 24.

[24a] *Hong Kong Tiger Standard,* Sept. 29, 1963.

[25] *Progress Report 1959/60,* para. 36.

[26] Commissioner of Police, *Annual Report, 1960/61,* para. 194.

[27] *Progress Report, 1959/60,* para. 37.

[28] *Ibid.,* para. 38.

CHAPTER V

TREATMENT OF DRUG ADDICTS

TREATMENT IN THE CORRECTIONAL SYSTEM

Since Hong Kong's facilities for voluntary treatment of narcotics ad-diction are still in the very early stages of development, most of the treatment facilities existing at the time of my visit were within the cor-rectional system — a fact that should not be misconstrued as evidence of a punitive attitude. As the Hong Kong Government states, "the imprison-ment of an addict is now regarded primarily as an opportunity to redeem him from his vice and to cure him of his addiction."[1]

However, as shown in recent legislation and in the special steps taken during the anti-narcotics drive, the Hong Kong Government is keenly aware of the temporary nature of this state of affairs. No doubt because of the undesirability of having to first imprison a man before giving him treatment, the Colony is steering nearer and nearer to voluntary treat-ment of the addict.

H.M. Prison (Tai Lam)

Within the prison system, the Government has established a special institution for addicts at Tai Lam in the New Territories. This prison has facilities for over 700 inmates,[2] who are housed in solidly constructed barracks originally put up for laborers working on the Tai Lam Water Reservoir. Since its inception in November 1958, a number of buildings and other facilities have been added, among them a swimming pool and a ball field (Ill. 12). While Tai Lam seemed rather bare-looking in the photos printed in earlier publications,[3] it looks now much greener as a result of the extensive tree-planting and gardening that have been going on. The prison is considered a minimum-security institution; the road

Illustration 12.
PART OF H.M. PRISON (TAI LAM)
On the ballfield (foreground) and hillside, older inmates and others fit only
for light work are weeding.

extending from Tai Lam Chung village to the reservoir goes right
through the institution and one frequently sees persons with waterbuffalos
or even vehicles on this road. Guards are stationed at the entrance to the
prison but they do not halt any people; when a car comes, its number is
noted but it is not stopped. The prison used to be completely open, I was
told, but when I visited it, part of the institution had been surrounded
by a fence. I was told that the purpose of this fence was not to keep
prisoners from escaping, but rather to keep strangers out of the prison.
Indeed, many of the prisoners' regular activities, such as going to the
administration building, to the gardening area, to the workshops or to the
mobile health units which regularly visit the institution, take them
outside this enclosed area. A prisoner would have no great trouble
escaping from either inside or outside of this area. Inmate groups assigned to work tasks are usually guarded by only a minimum number of
warders. The same degree of security is also used when prisoners work,
as they often do, in areas distant from the prison and difficult to keep

under surveillance such as reforestation areas or villages undergoing restoration. In spite of all the opportunity, the number of escapes has been very small. During the fiscal year of 1960 to 1961, two prisoners escaped from forestry working parties at Tai Lam and both were recaptured the day after they escaped.[4]

The institution is frequently inspected. Every day, the Superintendent makes a routine tour of the prison; once a week the Colony's Commissioner of Prisons visits it; and every two weeks Justices of the Peace also visit and, among other things, listen to the complaints of the prisoners.

Intake Policy

Not every addict prisoner in the Colony is sent to Tai Lam. The following conditions must be met, as a rule, before an addict can be admitted:

1. *Disease:* Men with active cases of organic diseases are, as far as possible, rejected.
2. *General Physical Condition:* Men who are chronically disabled or extremely emaciated may be rejected.
3. *Length of Addiction:* More recent addicts take precedence.
4. *Environment:* Certain addicts who are "thoroughly of undesirable character" may be rejected. This condition would largely apply to members of the secret societies, known gangsters, or persons with long criminal records, who are considered sociopaths. Addicts, who have committed both narcotics and other offenses, are admitted if they are drug users. Usually the prisoners at Tai Lam are "star offenders" — that is, first offenders or offenders with up to three convictions (only if these convictions are not serious or do not indicate that the offender is likely to become a habitual criminal).[5]

Since Tai Lam is considered as a desirable place to be imprisoned, once in a while an offender who is not an addict manages to end up temporarily at this institution. Thus, within the group of 502 inmates whom we investigated statistically there were two prisoners who were not drug users.[6]

Approach

The approach at Tai Lam, as in all the Hong Kong prisons I saw, is basically authoritarian in the belief that addicts need — and welcome — firm guidance. This authoritarian approach, for example, finds expression in the fact that prisoners stand "at attention" when an officer passes. All personnel wore uniforms,[7] with the exception of a few office clerks, the prison physician, and the newly introduced rehabilitation workers. The physician and rehabilitation workers may spend a certain amount of time on individualized observation of the personalities of the inmates and perhaps fulfill some needs for psychological treatment, though, with about 700 at Tai Lam, and with great difficulties of recruitment of rehabilitation workers, these possibilities are understandably limited. The administrative and custodial staff, on the other hand, generally probably have little personal relationship with the inmate population. A specialist in the Colony, well informed in American approaches, warned me that ethnic and cultural differences between Hong Kong and the United States should be taken into account before passing judgment on the type of authoritarian approach, which, at the present time, appears to be considered necessary for addicts in Hong Kong.

Some lectures are given for the prisoners. One meeting which I attended, was held for a newly arrived group gathered to hear the prison physician talk in Cantonese on the problems of narcotics. Although, if I understand correctly, they had been invited to ask questions, there was no active participation on the part of the prisoners.[8] I understand that similar sessions are held shortly before a group of prisoners is released.

The treatment program aims mainly at the rehabilitation of the inmate in the physical sense, *viz.* (a) "to free the prisoner from addiction in any particular field of indulgence, (b) to treat any disease complicated by addiction, (c) to rebuild physical strength and bring it up to normal standards".[9]

Fort sums up treatment at Tai Lam as consisting "mainly of work and a good diet",[10] or, as a leading Hong Kong prison official put it some time ago, "I am convinced that the three essentials for the speedy rehabilitation of drug addicts are good food, vigorous exercise in the form of work, and fresh air".[11]

Withdrawal

Inmates who arrive at Tai Lam, generally have already gone through withdrawal at Victoria Prison. Since, however, a prisoner's stay at Victoria is frequently very short, withdrawal symptoms may still be present in the new arrivals at Tai Lam. For this reason, new arrivals are frequently allowed a one-to-two-week rest period before being placed in the regular work schedule.

Work

Not only is outdoor work believed to be healthful for addicts, it is also believed to be "of the greatest value as rehabilitative training"[12] for them. The underlying principle is that a prisoner who sees his efforts turned to some useful purpose will have a better morale. For this reason, a number of very significant projects in the Colony — especially in the New Territories — have been completed by the inmates of Tai Lam. Among them are the following:

a. A retaining wall 110 feet long built to avoid silting of the farmers' paddy fields at So Kun Wat.
b. A collecting station for vegetable farmers built at Shu Kong Wai.
c. The restoration of Tin Tze Wai, an old walled village inhabited mainly by aged widows. (Two new houses were completed, two leaking houses repaired, 400 feet of a surface channel and a village path 270 feet long built, 200 feet of boundary wall repaired).
d. A road constructed at Yuen Tun.
e. A road built at Castle Peak Boys' Home.
f. Labor provided for the building of several cottages at Siu Lam as a settlement for cured addicts.[13]

Of particular importance among the projects is a reforestation program which the Prisons Department carries out on behalf of the Agriculture and Forestry Department. During World War II the Colony of Hong Kong, under foreign occupation, had been depleted of trees. Because of this, widespread tree-planting is now going on in the New

Territories, and prison labor is playing an important part in this task.[14] Approximately 120 prisoners are occupied daily in reforestation work — sometimes at considerable distance from the prison — and are driven to work in trucks along with a minimum number of guards. During the fiscal year 1960/61, Tai Lam prisoners planted over 300 000 gum, eucalyptus, and pine trees and cleared the terrain for 50 000 feet of fire barrier in the newly planted territory.[15]

During my stays, I was able to observe work crews and the sites of reforestation and construction projects, while both work was going on and after completion. As far as a layman can judge, the work appeared to be expertly done. I was especially impressed with the token number of guards present among various prisoner details at work so far away from the prison. I am sure it must have been quite impossible for the guards

Illustration 13.

TAI LAM RATTAN WORKERS IN AN OPEN SHED

to keep sight of all the prisoners in their charge, particularly among the man-sized bushes in the reforestation area or in the small alleys of an old Chinese walled village.

Inside Tai Lam — though not necessarily within the enclosure described earlier — a good deal of outdoor work is also done. The prison has an extensive program of improvements: construction of various types of structures, gardening, and maintenance work. Since a new women's prison is scheduled to be built in the immediate vicinity of Tai Lam, the administration will no doubt avail itself of addict prisoner manpower for the construction of this new facility.

Approximately eighty men are occupied in the "essential work" of maintaining the prison. Eight men work in the tailor shop, three in the shoemaker shop, and six in the kitchen.

Some types of work such as carpentry, bootmaking, and rattan work which would ordinarily be done indoors in other climates, can here be performed out-of-doors because of the subtropical climate (ill. 13).

All physically-able prisoners are required to work during their stay. Those who can do only light work — old men or men with tuberculosis not requiring hospitalization — do outdoor weeding and other light tasks. The prisoners work seven hours a day, from Monday through Friday, and a reduced schedule on Saturday, for which they receive a small remuneration: H.K. 40 cents a week for men who are hospitalized, 80 cents for ordinary manual laborers, and $ 1.20 for skilled workers, such as cooks. According to statistics dating from the spring of 1961, 3 out of 464 prisoners received pay as artisans, 331 as manual laborers, and 130 as hospital patients.

Although the prison does not have vocational training, many inmates are receiving on-the-job training in such fields as carpentry or masonry. For instance, men who had never been carpenters before had pre-manufactured in Tai Lam workshops the wooden parts for a new building at Lai Chi Kok Prison for Women; and masons, who had received their only training at Tai Lam, were busy putting it up on the site.

Recreation consists of movies once-a-week, sports events on the ball field and in the swimming pool, etc. Every day, local newspapers are supplied. The inmates receive free cigarette rations and have canteen facilities.

Illustration 14.

MOBILE DENTAL CLINIC PARKED ON THE PUBLIC ROAD LEADING THROUGH TAI
LAM PRISON

Villagers are passing through the institution while groups of inmates are waiting
for dental treatment.

Health Care

The generally emaciated appearance of drug addicts is well-known, and many arrive at Tai Lam in that state. There, as inmates, they receive an additional food allowance beyond the regular Hong Kong prison diet. By the time they are released, the inmates generally have put on a good deal of weight. For example, 460 inmates released during the quarter beginning April 1961 had gained and only one had lost weight — the average gain being 15.78 lbs.[16]

The prison has a full-time physician who diagnoses illnesses and treats all inmates except those who must be hospitalized on the outside for serious ailments. During 1960 there were 23 such serious cases.

Tai Lam is served regularly by several mobile medical units. A tuberculosis unit visits the prison twice a month, taking miniature X-ray pictures. Suspect cases are then referred to a chest specialist who also comes to Tai Lam twice a month. Once a week a social hygiene unit comes to administer venereal disease tests. (During 1960, 3 574 visits were made to this unit). A mobile dental unit (Ill. 14) comes once or twice a week. There is also a mobile eye clinic.

Other Aspects

Mail privileges are the same as in all Hong Kong prisons: each prisoner may send and receive one letter every four weeks.[17] However, the prisoners generally make very little use of their letter-writing privilege. Once-a-month visits by relatives or friends are permitted in accordance with prison rules. Although Tai Lam is sixteen miles away from Kowloon, about an hour's bus ride, frequent departures from the Jordan Ferry Terminal (this ferry service operates all day long between Victoria and Kowloon) brings Tai Lam within reasonably easy reach of the prisoners' relatives, most of whom live in those two cities. I understand however, that the once-a-month visits rule is not strictly enforced. In view of the distance traveled, whenever a member of a prisoner's family comes out to visit an inmate, visiting permission is practically never refused — even if the inmate has already filled his quota of visits.

Disciplinary Punishment

Corporal punishment, though permitted in Hong Kong not only by court order but also as a prison disciplinary measure, has not been used for the latter purpose in any of the Hong Kong correctional institutions since around 1952.[18]

There is no parole in Hong Kong, but if he behaves well each prisoner automatically receives an allowance off the time he has to serve. This "time off" is computed at the beginning of his sentence, and very rarely is it withheld as a disciplinary punishment at Tai Lam.

Most punishment inflicted consists in taking away privileges which make a prisoner's life more pleasant, e.g., visits to the movie or ball game, but it also consists in imposing extra duties. The number of inmates who receive disciplinary punishment at Tai Lam is indeed quite small. For instance, only 10 prisoners were punished during the quarter beginning October 1, 1960, and 11 during the quarter beginning January 1, 1961. The decision to deprive a prisoner of his privileges is made by the superintendent after the inmate is given a hearing. Severe cases are brought before the regular Hong Kong court, as in one of the two cases of escape mentioned earlier. In this instance, the man was sentenced to nine additional months of prison.

There seems to be remarkably little smuggling of narcotics into Tai Lam, though, as far as I know, the administration of spot checks was not practiced. It seems that only one case was discovered the year before my visit, when heroin was found on a prisoner working outside the prison. While such contraband may be a characteristic problem of some Western correctional institutions, its absence seems to be characteristic also of other Far Eastern institutions such as the addiction treatment centers on St. John's Island (Singapore) and at Macau. Why this is so may perhaps be explained by a statement which was made to me in Singapore, namely that the "atmosphere" of the Center was not favorable to smuggling. Prisoners, I was told, were so happy to be regaining their health that they were not in the mood to resume the narcotics habit, at least not while they were at the Center. Of course, as soon as they are released and exposed to their old milieus and its pressures, this picture may change.

Results

No definite figures exist by which to evaluate the treatment given prisoners at Tai Lam. This much *is* known. On July 1, 1961, 31 % (1 406) of the 4 510 persons who had been inmates at Tai Lam had been reconvicted and found to be drug users again and another 3% (116) had been reconvicted but showed no signs of addiction. Similarly, 68 per cent of the former inmates had not been reconvicted as of December 31, 1962, out of a total of 7 700.[19]

Other Correctional Institutions

In the year 1960/61, 18 255 offenders were sentenced to imprisonment by Hong Kong magistracies.[20] Among them were 11 663 persons (64 per cent) sentenced for narcotics offenses.

Assuming a considerable number of the latter were not users themselves (and I believe their number is small compared to the number of addicts and addicted pushers), the number of addicts who come before

the courts each year would still be much larger than could be accommo-
dated at Tai Lam Prison (capacity: 750 inmates). Thus, a few words
should also be said about other Hong Kong prisons.

Thanks to the opportunity generously given me by the Department
of Prisons, I was able to observe other Hong Kong prisons and to take
notes on the addicts found there.[21]

All Hong Kong prisons appeared to be run efficiently and in a
human way, although, to be sure, their particular form of authoritarian
orientation may not necessarily be applicable to institutions in all other
places. The features of the Hong Kong situation should not be misinter-
preted by applying foreign standards to them. As pointed out elsewhere,
they may be due to particular local conditions. That a progressive spirit
prevails in the Prison Administration can be seen, e.g. from the wide use
of open institutions in the Colony and the fact that the Administration
considers them suitable for almost all offenders with sentences up to
three years.

H. M. Prison (Victoria)

Victoria Prison is the Colony's classification and reception center
for male offenders. Since the Colony's judiciary works in a very speedy
manner, prisoners remain at Victoria for only one to two weeks as a rule.
Unless they receive a short-term sentence (under three months), after
conviction they are normally transferred from Victoria to another prison
to serve out the sentence.

TABLE XLII

ADMISSIONS AT VICTORIA PRISON FROM SEPT. 25 TO OCT. 21, 1961 *

	Number	%
Drug Addicts	626	72
Non-addicts	244	28
Total Admissions	870	100

* By courtesy of the Prison Department.

Table XLII shows, as an example, the number of drug addicts admitted
to Victoria Prison between September 25 and October 21, 1961. Of 870
inmates admitted, 72 % (626 persons) were drug addicts. As can be seen

TABLE XLIII

DISPOSITION OF DRUG ADDICTS ADMITTED TO VICTORIA PRISON FROM SEPTEMBER 25
TO OCTOBER 21, 1961 *

Classified for prison	Number	%
Tai Lam	168	27
Chi Ma Wan	104	17
Stanley	323	51
Victoria	31	5
Total	626	100

* By courtesy of the Prison Department.

from Table XLIII, 27 % of these 626 were transferred to Tai Lam. Five per cent who apparently had received short sentences remained at Victoria. Over 50 % were sent to Stanley, and 17 % to Chi Ma Wan. Although most offenders stay there only briefly, Victoria prison plays a very important role in the treatment of addicted prisoners. For one thing, their withdrawal takes place here. For a number of years only commercial tranquilizers, and no narcotics, have been given during the deprivation period; nor are narcotics used at any other time during the institutional stay. I was told that, if withdrawal symptoms are light (as they usually are), the men are sent out after a week or two by weekly transport to their final institutions without necessarily being completely relieved of their symptoms.

The Superintendent decides to which institution a prisoner should be sent. He does this "upon reception interview" (in accordance with Standing Order 562 of the Department of Prisons) and with the help of the offender's records. On the day of my visit, I was permitted to sit in on the intake interviews. Because of the number of prisoners, the interviews are necessarily brief. Understandably, they offer little opportunity for a deep probing of individual problems.

A detailed description of Victoria prison lies outside the scope of this report. Although it is the oldest penal institution of the Colony, many of its facilities were built after World War II, after some of the older buildings had been bombed out. Its hospital has about twenty beds (where I saw a few withdrawal cases with complications). As a separate unit, there is also a thirty-bed psychiatric observation ward which, however, is not extensively used for addicts. A complete reconstruction of Victoria as a reception and classification center is under consideration.[22]

H. M. Prison (Stanley)

Addicts sent to Stanley Prison are often members of secret societies or have a long record of convictions which would preclude profitable treatment at Tai Lam. It is a maximum-security institution and has been described as "architecturally the best security prison in the Commonwealth".[23] While it has only 1 579 cells, the roll call on the day of my visit (Nov. 10, 1961) totalled 3 092 prisoners. According to the Commissioner of Prisons, Stanley Prison has "been overcrowded ever since it was opened."[24] Indeed, this overcrowding has become even more aggravated because of the recent extension of penalties for the manufacture of narcotics. The prison administration hopes to end this overcrowding through the construction of two open prisons — one at Tong Fuk on the Island of Lantao and the other at Plover Cove in the New Territories — both sites located near areas in need of conservation work.[25]

As pointed out elsewhere, Stanley Prison does have some trouble with the smuggling-in of narcotics. According to an unpublished report for the period ending June 30, 1961, a campaign against drug smuggling in prison had met with considerable success. I understand that the amounts of drugs found being smuggled into the institution were very small.

Under the Emergency (Detention Orders) Regulations, 1956, Chap. 241, a separate block at Stanley is used for detainees (52 on the day of my visit) liable to deportation. Where the enforcement of a deportation order is impracticable — especially with respect to the political situation on the Chinese mainland, — the Governor in Council orders that the person be detained, should it be contrary to the public interest for him to remain at-large in the Colony. A number of gangsters from mainland China are being held under this provision, among them possibly some connected with the drug traffic.

H.M. Prison (Chi Ma Wan)

As we have seen in Table XLIII, 17 % of the addicted prisoners were sent to this new open institution located on the still very undeveloped island of Lantao. As at Tai Lam, a health-oriented atmosphere prevails. Able-bodied inmates are engaged primarily outdoors in the construction of roads, bridges, pipelines, buildings, and in reforestation. So far, usually "star prisoners," i.e., those sentenced to three years or less imprisonment, are sent to Chi Ma Wan.

H.M. Prison (Lai Chi Kok)

Lai Chi Kok is the only prison for the Colony's female offenders. On the day of my visit, its roll call was 216, more than its designated capacity. The overcrowding of the institution was caused in part by an increase in the number of female drug offenders — though not necessarily of women addicts — who were imprisoned during the recent anti-narcotics drive. It was made even worse by the installation of a large mechanized laundry, which took away from the limited space available in the prison. In this laundry the inmates do much of the washing for the Colony's Medical and Health Departments.[26] The planned construction of a new women's prison near Tai Lam is expected to relieve this overcrowding.

An estimated 60 % of the inmates have been involved in opium or heroin offenses — 45 % as drug addicts and 15 % as non-users sentenced for drug offenses (in Hong Kong women are used on a large scale as carriers of drugs).[27] On the day of my visit, prison officials estimated that most likely all the inmates in the institution on that particular day could have suitably been sent to an open institution if such an institution were available to women.

Probation

The probation services for both adults and juveniles in the Colony are under the Department of Social Welfare. I visited the Probation Department at the Kowloon Magistracy. Before July, 1961, by order of the Hong Kong courts, a limited number of drug addicts were put on probation after the Probation Department, having made a pre-sentence investigation, had expressed its willingness to accept them as charges. From January to the end of June, 1960, 20 drug users were under the supervision of the Probation Department; of these 17 (85 %) had completed their probation satisfactorily and 3 (15 %) were considered "doubtful". During the second half of 1960, 45 drug addicts were put on

probation with similar success rates. No results were arrived at for the
48 drug addicts placed on probation during the first half of 1961. Pro-
bationers accepted by the Department were often remanded for exami-
nation and then placed, as a rule, with such government clinics as the
Out-patient Department of Kowloon Hospital; others requiring more
medical attention were confined as in-patients for two weeks.

After June 1961, the Department of probation changed its policy and
discontinued recommending probation for drug addicts on the grounds
that it lacked sufficient facilities for dealing with them successfully. The
Department also believed that the establishment of Tai Lam Prison and
the voluntary drug addiction treatment centers provided better medical
facilities than it could provide.

On my second trip, I was told that the policy of not recommending
drug addicts for probation is unchanged.

Voluntary Treatment

In discussing voluntary treatment of narcotics addicts in Hong Kong,
I would like again to bring up the controversy that is still raging over the
so-called "British system" of permitting physicians to administer supportive doses of narcotics to addicts under certain strict conditions. [28]
One of the arguments that has been brought forward is that British
practice would not work in a country such as the United States, where
the number of addicts is many times greater than in England. To prove
this argument, its proponents have pointed to Hong Kong. Hong Kong
they claim, has a large number of addicts despite the fact that it is a
British colony and is thus subject to the British "system" of treating
addicts. [28a]

We may disregard the semantic question whether the British approach
can properly be called a "system"; the British hardly use this expression
when they speak of their handling of narcotics matters. Quite different
meanings have been attached to it by different persons such as the total
of existing regulations and practices, clinics, the method of "gradual"
withdrawal, etc. Let us briefly examine the differences and similarities
between the British and American approaches to the problem.

As far as laws and regulations are concerned, both countries permit a
physician to cure addiction on condition that when he prescribes or

administers narcotics to a patient, he does so in strict accordance with his professional practice. Both countries agree that mere gratification of an addict is not regarded as a legitimate professional practice. Despite these similarities, however, the two countries do differ in their definition of a physician's "professional practice". The British, in accordance with the recommendation made in 1926 by the Departmental Committee on Morphine and Heroin Addiction of the British Ministry of Health (the so-called "Rolleston Report"), will permit a doctor to administer a drug

> "where it has been demonstrated, after a prolonged attempt at cure, that the use of the drug cannot safely be discontinued entirely on account of the severity of the withdrawal symptoms produced" or "where it has been similarly demonstrated that the patient, while capable of leading a useful and relatively normal life when a certain minimum dose is regularly administered, becomes incapable of this when the drug is entirely discontinued." [29]

In order to avoid abuses, the British physician deciding upon the administration of narcotics in such instances is advised to obtain a second medical opinion. [30] Twenty-five years after these recommendations were made, the Brain Report of 1961 reaffirmed this approach. [31]

It is the issue of the application of minimum maintenance doses by qualified physicians on which our discussion focuses, and, to limit the topic further, we will here consider only the question of longterm application in the two cases outlined in the Rolleston Report. We are, in particular, not concerned with the question of gradual vs. abrupt withdrawal or with clinics for the administration of narcotics.

In the United States, confusion over interpretation of the Harrison Act of 1915 and the existing jurisprudence on the matter has led to uncertainty. "Official" law enforcement agency interpretation of the provisions of this Act discouraged physicians from treating addicts with moderate supportive doses of narcotics and threatened physicians with criminal prosecution, even when they were acting in good faith and in strict conformity with medical standards. As interpreted by the U.S. Supreme Court, the Harrison Act permits a physician to give a narcotics addict maintenance doses, but only a criminal trial can determine whether the physician is doing this legally and in strict accordance with medical ethics. The physician, then, always risks conviction, consequent imprisonment, and loss of license. Under these circumstances, American medical practicioners understandably often preferred not to get involved at all in the matter and frequently turned their backs on addicts. Because of this situation, it is claimed that they have not been able to maintain control over problems of narcotics addiction, as have their English colleagues. [32]

In Hong Kong, the *Dangerous Drugs Ordinance,* together with the *Dangerous Drugs Regulations,* permits the physician, the dentist, and the veterinarian to prescribe and administer narcotics as part of their professional practice, and permits the druggist to fill their prescriptions. [33] This policy has been reconfirmed in the wording of the various amendments which always exempt from their criminal provisions the cases where dangerous drugs are manipulated under medical direction or supervision.

The British recommendations of the British Ministry of Health would not apply automatically to Hong Kong, officials stated. Of course, it was possible to make such recommendations applicable, — possibly by rewriting them in light of the special conditions of the Colony, — but this had never been done.

The Government has gone on record in favor of isolation, and against out-patient treatment, of narcotics addicts. [34] I asked health officials what would happen if a doctor were to administer — *bona fide* and upon consultation with a second physician — maintenance doses as in the above cited cases mentioned in the Rolleston report, especially to an addict who, after many cures have failed, has nonetheless demonstrated that he is capable of leading a useful and relatively normal life when certain minimum doses of narcotics are regularly administered to him. I was informed that such a case had never come to the attention of the authorities, if it were to, a disciplinary board, composed of physicians, would have to decide whether or not such treatment is professionally acceptable.

Hong Kong authorities check carefully the prescribing and administering of dangerous drugs by Hong Kong physicians. Those who abuse their privileges thus come readily to the attention of the authorities.

During the last year, there had been only four cases of such abuse, I was told. One case was still pending; in two others, two doctors had been called in and had been admonished by the Director of Public Health. In the fourth case, the Disciplinary Board had, as punishment, suspended the physician's dangerous drugs privileges for the duration of three months. Considering that there are approximately 1 200 medical practitioners in the Colony,[35] four cases must be considered as a very low number. Without any general threats of persecution from law enforcement agencies, the medical profession of the Colony has not seen fit to indulge in flagrant large-scale prescribing of narcotics.

On the whole, the Hong Kong physicians with whom I spoke gave the impression that, to them, no problem or controversy exists with respect to the provisions of the *Dangerous Drugs* legislation. As seen by everybody in the Colony, these provisions clearly define the rights of the medical profession; the upper courts need not be called upon to interpret the legislation.

Statistics have not shown an increase of actual addiction during the last few years.[36] Furthermore, even if it is true that Hong Kong has a large number of addicts — actually we do not know how many there are — conditions in the Colony do not prove the alleged failure of the British approach in the presence of wide-spread drug abuse.

The other argument sometimes used against application of the British approach to the United States — the wide cultural difference between the two countries — is not supported by Hong Kong either. There is less of a cultural difference between London and New York, (both of which have a long Anglo-Saxon tradition) than there is between London and Hong Kong, 99 per cent of whose population is Chinese.

Institutions for Voluntary Treatment

Specialized institutions for the voluntary treatment of drug addicts are new in Hong Kong. The *1959 White Paper* had mentioned such facilities as a future possibility, and, although plans existed at that time, none had been realized.[37] Then, on September 8, 1960, the *Drug Addict Treatment and Rehabilitation Ordinance, 1960,* was issued under Proclamation No. 2 of 1961. According to this ordinance, the Governor of the Colony might declare any public property or, upon application of the owner, private property an Addiction Treatment Center "for the detention, custody, treatment, care and rehabilitation of addicts." The superintendent or assistant superintendent has to be a registered medical practitioner whose powers and functions could be delegated only to another registered medical practitioner. [38] The decision to admit a patient lies with the superintendent.

Of interest is the application for admission which the prospective patient has to fill out. Among other features, the patient has to acknowledge that he is under a legally binding obligation to remain and be detained against his will for a period not exceeding six months from the date of his first admission, if so required by the superintendent. Should he absent himself without permission, he may be retaken forcibly. In case of escape, a patient may be retaken within 28 days. [39] Further, the superintendent may require an applicant to enter into a bond of up to H.K. $ 35 000 "to secure the continued presence." [40] Patients with sufficient means may have to pay for the cost of their treatment and to enter into a bond for the amount of this cost.

Section 14 of the ordinance establishes an Addiction Treatment Appeal Board, consisting of the Director or Deputy Director of Medical and Health Services as chairman, the Secretary for Chinese Affairs and the Director of Social Welfare or their representatives as *ex officio* members, and up to four other members to be appointed by the Governor. The Board has courtlike powers to receive evidence on oath, to issue summonses, and decide appeals — to which a patient who "is aggrieved by his detention" is entitled. [41] (Apparently, "aggrievement"' refers only to the deprivation of liberty rather than to the type of treatment being administered, since it is provided that, if the court should allow the appeal, it shall order the patient's discharge as well.) [42] In the case of other complaints such as refusal of admission, there is no provision for appeal. Rough treatment or wilful neglect of patients by attendants, nurses, servants, and other persons makes them liable to a fine of up to H.K. $ 2 000 or to imprisonment of up to two years. [43] According to Section 5, two or more Treatment Centre Visitors have to inspect each center at least once a month. They also have the right to file appeals with the Board. The Hong Kong Governor in Council may issue regulation for the implementation of the Ordinance. [44]

The Voluntary Addiction Treatment Centre at Castle Peak Hospital

Within one month after March 1, 1961, the date the *Drug Addict Treatment and Rehabilitation Ordinance* went into operation, the treatment center at Castle Peak (a separate closed ward of 60 beds in a newly built psychiatric hospital) was opened. [45] Obviously conceived as an experiment, the Castle Peak centre was described as a "pilot scheme in voluntary treatment." [46]

There have been some misgivings about the fact that the Centre forms part of a mental institution and the staff seems to be especially unhappy about the fact that the Centre is close to the ward for disturbed women.

Originally, the Centre consisted of one closed, separate ward with sixty beds but, considering the type of patients, it was soon found out that a staff of only five could not control so large a group. Since then, there have been two wards with a maximum of 30 beds each.

In addition to the psychiatric staff, there are 2 charge nurses, 6 staff nurses, and 12 hospital orderlies. Two additional persons take care of occupational therapy. The pre-intake investigations and after-care supervision is in the hands of an almoner who has 3 assistants. [47]

As I understand it, a random population of addicts was admitted in the beginning. This, however, seemed to be unsatisfactory:

"Strict rules to prevent the smuggling in of drugs had to be enforced. Visitors, after screening, were kept under observation all the time and the number of visits controlled. Children were not allowed in. Patients were forbidden to keep money on themselves or in the ward, cigarettes were rationed and smoking allowed only at certain hours. It was necessary to control cigarette smoking because of the practice of 'firing the ack ack gun'. Matches were also forbidden to forestall secretive 'playing the mouth organ'. Lavatory doors and all cupboards were kept locked. Patients and lockers were subjected to surprise searches. Patients were not allowed their own clothing, nor any food from visitors. ... Gambling had to be stopped, partly because patients used cigarettes as stakes. All cigarettes exceeding a certain number found ... were confiscated.

The restriction that had to be enforced inevitably resulted in indignation, disobedience and even hostility. About a third of the cases had experienced life in prison before and many had social characteristics typical of established drug addicts — evasiveness, unreliability, proneness to impulsive action and lack of thought for the future. Moreover, gangs based on dialect groups soon grew up. On different occasions, there were mass refusals to go into the garden, to obey the instructions of staff in charge of walking parties, to take food, or do work. Sometimes, infrequently, the junior ward staff were threatened with physical violence. On one occasion, general rowdiness led to the police being called."

This early phase of treatment was most trying to the staff who felt that the difficulties were caused by the fact that most patients resented detention after regaining their well-being and putting on weight.

Thus, shortly before my first visit to the Centre, the intake policy was changed:

"Selection of suitable cases for admission was necessary in view of the large numbers coming forward and the need to ensure that the limited facilities available were not wasted on incurable cases, or those insincere over treatment."

Particular attention is given to avoiding intake under pressure from courts and other sources (though a patient's will to be cured may sometimes be influenced by his family).

It is indeed this very careful intake policy, together with an attractive incentive pay scheme, which has been credited with making the patients more amenable.

Criteria for selection included: (1) Promise of employment after cure; (2) Good work record; (3) Freedom from serious physical or mental disease; (4) Good previous personality; (5) Relatively brief history of addiction; (6) Comparatively good response to previous attempts at cure, if any; (7) Addiction arising as a result of therapy; (8) Evidence of family support rather than social isolation; (9) Absence of a serious criminal record; and, (10) Genuine desire to get cured.

An addict wishing to be admitted to the Centre is examined medically and psychiatrically, and is also questioned in detail by the almoner, who looks into the patient's personal history and his history of employment and addiction. It has been observed that patients reveal to the almoner, in most cases, their past difficulties with the law, though this information may not necessarily be accurate. The psychiatrist then sees the report and makes the necessary decisions.

Only a small fraction of the applicants can be accepted.[48] There were approximately 1 400 registrations at the time of my second visit and I was told that patients may sometimes have to wait two years before entering the hospital. I raised the question of what would happen to a registered patient who was found with drugs before he had the opportunity to begin treatment. No special provision exists for this situation; such an addict would be sent to court, I was told.

Before admission, the patient is told that he has to remain an in-patient for up to six months, and he has to sign a statement promising this. It is also made clear to him that the Centre will not readmit him if he relapses after the treatment.

Until the end of the year 1962/63, only 34 patients had been requested to pay for their treatment (H.K. $ 2.— per day, i.e., $ 35 U.S. cents); only one patient had been asked to sign a bond prior to admission (out of a total of 284 admissions the Centre had made by the middle of 1963).

The first part of the treatment consists in the withdrawal of the drug whereby methodone is administered. Withdrawal symptoms are measured objectively by the Himmelfarb Scale of Intensity of Abstinence Symptoms, and are generally found present, though mild or moderate. No serious problems have arisen in the two years of the Centre's operation as far as the withdrawal stage is concerned.

It is the second stage of rehabilitation where the above mentioned difficulties have been experienced. In this stage, psychiatric individual treatment plays its part; if I understand it correctly, experiences with group therapy have not always been encouraging.

The Centre's leaders pointed out in the 1961/62 report that:

"The central problem for the administration is how to achieve a fruitful balance between repressive discipline and therapeutic rapport. Under our present circumstance it would seem wiser to emphasize the former in handling a group of this nature . . . After due experimentation it was thought fit for Drs. Y and Z to undertake the basic responsibilities of psychotherapy and for Dr. X to initiate disciplinary action when need arose. It was found that this division of function developed in such a manner that the almoners naturally became associated with psychotherapeutic activities, while the ward staff had inevitably to ensure obedience and respect for regulations. The punishments eventually standardized were: deprivation of dietary extras, of cigarettes, of privileges like walks and swimming, and also confinement to a single room."

The centre did not want to discharge trouble makers. As we have seen, all patients upon admission had to sign that they would stay at treatment center for six months. If making trouble would lead to an early discharge, all an uncooperative patient would have to do in order to get released was to create disorder.

Just as at Tai Lam Prison, great significance is attributed to the work program, here called "occupational therapy". Contrary to Tai Lam, however, the work does not take place in an open setting. [48a] Because the men have their well established occupations (and usually their jobs are held for them until after their release), there is no need for vocational training. As to the actual work itself, it was found that the patients work and behave best in small groups of approximately six men. Work includes broom-making, rattan work and tailoring. As to the latter, lined bedjackets, dressing gowns and other garments for hospital use are made. The workmanship is described as of high standard.

While the addicts are institutionalized, their families are told to turn, in case of difficulties, not directly to the patients but to the almoner in order to protect the patients from undue worrying. Some patients, however, do start worrying, about their families or jobs, and it is here, where the Centre makes use of its authority to grant leaves of absence. After each leave, the patient must undergo a nalline test in order to find out whether he used narcotics during his absence from the Centre.

At the present time, the Centre is again in a stage of transition. It is now becoming the reception center for the treatment institution on Shek Kwu Chau Island, described below. According to the new mode of operation, the patients spend the first four weeks at Castle Peak where they receive withdrawal treatment (and general medical treatment, where necessary) and then complete their cure on the island.

The Castle Peak Addiction Treatment Centre is also the place where, at the present time, practically all of Hong Kong's narcotics research takes place. Studies include the following:

(a) Main initiating factors of addiction. A study of 62 unselected cases admitted, concentrating on psychiatric aspects;

(b) Identification of stabilized narcotics "users";

(c) Aversion treatment to prevent relapses;

(d) Etiological study of 170 cases (exploratory);

(e) Follow-up of 314 cases as long as possible;

(f) Quantitative relationships of the Nalline Test;

(g) Systematic study of X-ray changes in the lungs of addicts before and after undergoing treatment;

(h) Epidemiological study of 1000—1200 cases.

Shek Kwu Chau Rehabilitation Centre

In 1959, the Working Committee for the Aid, Treatment, and Rehabilitation of Drug Addicts was formed under the chairmanship of the Hon. Dr. A. M. Rodrigues; it applied to the Government for the use of Shek Kwu Chau Island as a center for the treatment and rehabilitation of drug addicts. In July, 1960, after their application was approved, the Society for the Aid and Rehabilitation of Drug Addicts (S.A.R.D.A.) was established. With support from the Hong Kong Government, from organizations and individuals, the Society established a rehabilitation center on Shek Kwu Chau, an island about twelve miles from Victoria and Kowloon. The inauguration took place on April 23, 1963; the first ten patients were admitted on June 10, 1963.

Originally it had been planned to start with a considerably larger group of inmates, but these plans had been changed. When I visited the island in September 1963, there were approximately 70 inmates there. It is planned to increase the number of patients gradually until the Centre's capacity of 250 is reached.

As Map II shows, the island has, at present, a dormitory where the patients sleep in rooms accommodating about ten persons, a dining hall (which also serves as a hall for recreational events) with a modern kitchen, and a hospital which also houses the Social Welfare Officer's office. There are also a laundry, staff quarters, a water system consisting of a reservoir, dams and pumping facilities, a pier, and connecting roads.

The patients were sent there from the Castle Peak Centre in order to undergo the second stage of rehabilitation, "the restitution of physical condition and the improvement of the mental outlook",[49] the final stage to be provided through after-care following the patients release.

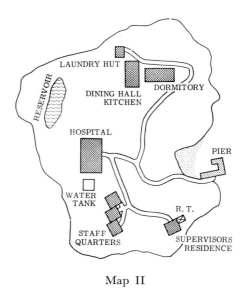

Map II

THE ADDICTION TREATMENT CENTER ON SHEK KWU CHAU ISLAND

The Social Welfare Officer holds individual consultations and group meetings; for the rest the program includes, like Castle Peak, occupational therapy. A good deal of the latter consists of work on the upkeep and on improvements of the Centre itself — road building, leveling the ground, vegetable gardening, making iron beds, painting, kitchen work, laundering, and there is also a sewing workshop. The patients' daily — program (Summer) is as follows:

6.00 a.m.	Rising bell, wash, make bed, clean dormitory, etc.
7.00 a.m.	Tea or milk. Breakfast (porridge or salted provisions)
7.30 a.m.	Occupational therapy
10.00 a.m.	Refreshment (30 minutes)
10.30 a.m.	Resume occupational therapy
11.30 a.m.	Cease occupational therapy
12.15 p.m.	Lunch (3 dishes and soup)
3.00 p.m.	Occupational therapy
4.30 p.m.	Refreshment (30 minutes)
5.00 p.m.	Resume occupational therapy
6.00 p.m.	Cease occupational therapy
7.00 p.m.	Dinner (3 dishes and soup)
9.00 p.m.	Bathing, prepare for bed
10.00 p.m.	Lights out

No winter program had as yet been established.

There was no resident physician on the island, only two medical orderlies. The Hon. Chairman of S.A.R.D.A., a prominent Hong Kong physician, is the Medical Director of the Centre. For psychiatric services, the staff of Castle Peak is available. In case of emergency, patients can be transferred — if necessary in a minimum of time by helicopter — to hospitals on nearby Cheung Chau island or to Hong Kong itself.

I visited the island on a Sunday when no work was going on; the men were receiving visits from their families in a shed near the newly established pier. Such visits are permitted once a week, the visitors taking a ferry boat to one of the neighboring islands from which they are picked up. The men are also permitted to write and receive letters without limitation; however all the incoming and outgoing mail is censored.

One month before my visit, the Centre had begun to discharge patients. Altogether, 27 discharges had already been made until then. A discharge is regularly preceded by a leave of absence. Upon return, the patient is given a nalline test; if this test does not show any narcotics consumption, the patient is discharged and placed under after-care.

The entire staff on the island amounts to approximately 25 persons, among them eight watchmen, hired especially in view of the possibility of smuggling-in of narcotics. [49a]

The Narcotics Treatment Center at Rennie's Mill

Occasionally, there have been other small-scale treatment institutions, often sponsored by idealistic religious bodies which have given in-patient treatment to drug addicts volunteering for this treatment. I visited the Treatment Center at Rennie's Mill, situated at Junk Bay in the New Territories. This Center is supported by the Norwegian Lutheran Mission with the sum of H.K. $ 8 000 per year (approximately U.S. $ 1 400). It is directed by the Rev. Agnar Espegren.

Rennie's Mill is a settlement of approximately 8 000—9 000 persons which houses mainly former members of the Chinese Nationalist Army and their dependent families who had escaped to Hong Kong in the course of the conquest of mainland China by the Communist forces. The socio-economic status of this group is low and so is their general health. A number of organizations, nearly all of them church sponsored, are giving medical help to the residents of Rennie's Mill through the Junk Bay Medical Relief Council. How much or how little addiction there is in this TB-ridden settlement, with its discouraged ex-military men, nobody knows.

The Center gives free treatment to addicts when the director is convinced that they sincerely wish to be cured.

There were twenty-four male, middle-aged patients there at the time of my visit, all quartered in one large locked-up room, which, together with a side room for equipment and the Director's office, constitute the Center. A watchman supervises the patients day and night. As a rule, the patients remain at the institution three months. During the first withdrawal, which usually takes ten days, a Chinese medicine called "...... Anti-Narcotic Cough Essence" and produced by a Hong Kong firm, is administered with gradual reduction in dosage.

The Center does not provide work for the patients, but there are regularly religious activities, such as Bible study and prayers. Occasionally, the men are taken out on walks with the watchman as a guard. Medical supervision is provided by a physician from the nearby Haven of Hope Sanatorium.

Out of the group registered at the time of my visit, 4—5 men had left the institution prematurely. Altogether, approximately 800 addicts have passed through the Center. The Rev. Espegren had no illusions about a large number of cases cured permanently by this treatment; he estimated, however, that perhaps fifteen per cent of the cases were cured.

Formerly, addict patients agreed to being fettered in order to resist their craving, and I was shown implements used for this purpose. In the last few years, however, this practice has been discontinued.

Aftercare

The presently existing services for aftercare are provided separately depending on whether the ex-addicts are released from correctional or voluntary institutions. On the whole, everybody agrees that the services as they exist at the present time are still far away from fulfilling the after-care needs of the Colony. All the services are still relatively new and the difficulties in improving and expanding them are not only of a financial nature. There is a great shortage of trained personnel, and the available workers have to cope with difficulties not always known in other places, such as the time consuming task of locating the many patients who have no fixed abode.

Aftercare for Tai Lam Prisoners

Aftercare of former drug users released from Tai Lam prison may be either under private auspices or under the auspices of the Prison Department. The Prison Department, which had already had an aftercare service for its training centers, extended this service to Tai Lam Prison inmates in 1959/60. Former Tai Lam prisoners may receive aftercare for twelve months after release. Five full-time social welfare officers had been assigned to Tai Lam; the Prison Department always has considerable difficulty in recruiting these workers. According to an advertisement that appeared in the Hong Kong press, social welfare workers must have a recognized academic degree, preferably in arts or sociology, must be under 35 years old, speak and write English, be able to write Chinese and speak fluent Cantonese. Knowledge of additional Chinese dialects and practical social work experience are desirable. The salary of these workers started at H.K. $ 765,— (or about U.S. $ 135,—) a month. Their duties were "To undertake social work (mainly outdoors) in connection with prisoners/inmates and to supervise persons released from Prisons and

Training Centers".[50]

The social welfare workers have an office at Tai Lam prison where interviews are held, not only with inmates but also with their relatives at the occasion of their visits to the institution. During the inmates' stay at Tai Lam the workers also service their families. About two weeks after an inmate's admission, the workers hold their first interview with him. (Initially, this interview took place immediately after the inmate's arrival, but this practice had to be changed because so many men still had withdrawal symptoms at that time.) As a rule, workers spend four working days at the institution, and the rest of the week in the field making visits to the homes of the released prisoners and their families.

In view of the scarcity of qualified workers, aftercare can be provided for only a limited number of former addicts, selected jointly by the Superintendent of Tai Lam Prison, the prison physician, and the social welfare workers acting as members of a Board of Aftercare. Usually, two hearings are provided for in each case, but many inmates have already been disqualified at the outset.[51]

As a rule, all former inmates are visited once a month as a part of the aftercare period with the exception of the so-called "good cases" who, in the workers' opinion, do not have to be visited as often.

In one of the unpublished reports, which I was given the privilege to read, the aftercare techniques for juveniles and young persons are compared with those for former inmates of Tai Lam prison. Young people should be approached with friendliness and understanding and the worker should "to a certain extent 'sail along with the wind and tide'." With ex-addicts, however, there should be a "tinge of forcefulness."

The following is an account of one of the sessions of the Board of Aftercare which I was given the opportunity to attend:

The first question put to each candidate was whether he actually wished to receive aftercare. Of the ten men being reviewed, one answered negatively, saying he felt that visits from the rehabilitation workers might interfere with his future employment. Although attempts were made to reassure him that this fear was ungrounded, he insisted on refusing aftercare. (This fear, I understand, is expressed quite frequently. Another reason for an inmate's rejection of aftercare is that he fears his family may learn about his former drug use and prison sentence. Since

Chinese men are often absent from their home for long periods of time because of their work, many families of inmates do not know of their addiction and imprisonment.)

Of the nine remaining who said they wished to receive aftercare, three were rejected, five accepted, and one case was postponed for further investigation. Two rejections were based on the fact that the men did not have a fixed address; the third was rejected because he had a history of twenty years of addiction and was considered unsuitable. The practice of rejecting persons without a fixed address — they usually comprise about 70 % of the candidates — may be regrettable, but it is quite understandable from a practical viewpoint. Owing to unstable housing conditions and the wide distances to be travelled, workers already spend an estimated fifty per cent of the time reserved for field work not only in going to and coming from the towns where their charges live but also in searching for their homes.

Of the five acceptances, one was based on special consideration of the needs of the prisoner's family, although he himself was considered a poor risk; another was based on the fact that the man lived with his family in a resettlement area. As mentioned before, tenants may be evicted from resettlement areas if they use drugs, but if the man is accepted for aftercare, such evictions will not take place.

It is still too early to evaluate the success of the limited aftercare program. On September 30, 1961, about one and a half years after the initiation of this service, a total of 114 cases had been accepted. Of these, 19 persons were discharged after twelve months of aftercare, 11 were reconvicted for drug offenses, and one for another offense. All the offenses took place during the aftercare period. Five known cases reverted to drug use — one of them during supervision, the remaining four after release. These seventeen known failures constituted only 14 per cent of the 114 aftercare cases, temporarily, at least, a promising success rate. Nevertheless, it should be remembered that, for all practical purposes, only the "cream-of-the-crop" — in the above instance, only 6 per cent of a total of 1 864 cases — receives aftercare.[52]

The Hong Kong Discharged Prisoners' Aid Society

Since the Prison Department's aftercare service serves only a small percentage of the men discharged annually from Tai Lam Prison, the services of the Discharged Prisoners' Aid Society form a most valuable supplement. In particular, the Society working in close cooperation with the authorities, can give help of various kinds to prisoners without fixed abode who, as we have seen, were not eligible for the Prison Department's aftercare service. The present Welfare Officer of the Society, Mr. C. O. Tsang, was drawn from the Prisons Department and previously a Rehabilitation Officer at Tai Lam Prison.

The H.K.D.P.A.S. cooperates closely with several other agencies, such as the Salvation Army and CARITAS-Hong Kong, and serves as a coordinator among the organizations involved. It provides, among other prison welfare services, aid to families of institutionalized men. The Society also assists the police in selected cases of police supervision frequently ordered by the Courts for dangerous offenders upon their release from prison. It places its "hostels" at the disposition of the Probation Department for certain of their cases.

The H.K.D.P.A.S. begins its care long before an offender's release from an institution. Every prisoner in a Hong Kong institution is given a card which, translated into English reads as follows:

> "If, after leaving the prison you have any problems that you cannot solve yourself and if you would like this Association to give you assistance or aid, please apply to the Superintendent of the Prison for an interview with our workers who make weekly prison visits. They will give you as much assistance as they possibly can.
>
> The Hong Kong Discharged Prisoners'
> Aid Society."[53]

Among other services, H.K.D.P.A.S. will furnish men, upon discharge, with referrals to other social agencies, find accommodations for them, help them obtain licenses, and also help with capital .

Since the Society cannot handle all the requests it receives, it selects its charges. There is now a staff of six caseworkers; in the last President's report, the opinion was expressed that three times as many were needed.[54] They interviewed about 12 342 prisoners in 1962/63 either in prison or in the Society's case work centers, and made a total of 3 710 house visits. During that period, the Society gave general assistance to 2 855 ex-prisoners and found employment for 652.[55]

The H.K.D.P.A.S. operates on funds obtained from its membership and from special fund-raising drives. It also receives subsidies from the Social Welfare Department of the Colony. Government subventions amounted to H.K. $ 165 000 in the year ending March 31, 1963.[56]

While believing that "the responsibility for the general rehabilitation of former drug addicts should be undertaken by separate and distinct organizations",[57] the Society has always accepted select cases from Tai Lam Prison (though not necessarily many cases of ex-addicts from other Hong Kong prisons). Only recently, it expressed its readiness to expand its services for ex-addicts,[58] a group that forms the large majority of the Colony's prison population.

In attempting to help them, the H.K.D.P.A.S., tries to

"be extra careful and alert especially when the majority of our clients who applied to us for assistance have a history of drug addiction. We aim at assisting and rehabilitating a displaced person into society, and not to assist in any way to relapsing and indulging in drug-taking. The problem is already acute as it is, and we are doing everything within our capacity to help solve this problem, and not to further aggravate the situation. Easy procurement of money without personal effort could mean inducement to return to one's former bad habits."[59]

Of all the benefits the H.K.D.P.A.S. offers former prisoners, its employment and hostel services are two of the most important. At the Annual General Meeting of the Society in 1961, Mr. Brook Bernacchi, then Chairman (who, incidentally, is also an officer of the Society for the Aid and Rehabilitation of Drug Addicts), made the following statement:

"The need to ensure that discharged prisoners are placed in employment as quickly as possible is quite paramount. Fortunately this had not proved difficult during the past year thanks to the cooperation of a considerable number of employers who have agreed to take men of this category. What is more we find that an ex-prisoner who is making good in employment is frequently able to introduce to his employer two or three other friends, also discharged prisoners, whom he would have met in prison and we find that he is careful not to introduce men who afterwards let us down. I must however appeal for more public cooperation in this matter. Once it gets known that an employer is engaging a few discharged prisoners loose talk develops to the effect that he has a bunch of 'laan Tsais' (that is rascal) for workmen. When this happens not only are the ex-prisoners themselves disheartened but other employers naturally make trouble and the employer finds that the local public opinion prevents him from engaging any more discharged prisoners. This situation is not serious at the moment but there are signs that it has occurred and steps must be taken to combat any such adverse public reactions." [60]

In the following year, he warned:

"We must also guard against yet another group who regard the employment of discharged prisoners as a means of obtaining cheap labour." [61]

By means of three hostels in Ngan Hon, Tsuen Wan, and Shanshuipo, the Society helps provide discharged prisoners with lodgings for a maximum period of six months. The daily average population in these hostels between April 1 and June 30, 1963, was 13, 11.5 and 6.5, considerably lower than their capacity of approximately 20 men each. The reason why these hostels are not filled to capacity is that the Society is highly selective, and does not admit those who have had "an unfavorable history of narcotics drug addiction." [62]

In 1961, I was shown the hostel at Shanshuipo which consisted of one large room approximately 40' × 15' filled with double bunks, a small side room where prisoners had set up individual burners to cook their food, and a washroom. Since then, this system has been changed. The cooking of meals is now arranged on a communal basis. One reason for this change was that "it could be a deterrent for those who may otherwise spend this money on drugs rather than food." [63] In a corner of the big room, a small area had been partitioned off for the supervisor who was a former house father in a boys' training school. On the day of my visit, the hostel housed fourteen people, four of whom happened to be present. Of these, one was an old man whom I recognized had been an inmate at Tai Lam and who had just been released. Although he was unemployable (arrangements had been made to transfer him within a few days to a home for old people), he had been accepted temporarily at the hostel.

Shanshuipo hostel, like the other hostels, is located near an industrial area where employment can be secured by the D.P.A.S. for its residents. They pay nothing until they have received their first pay check. Once they have been paid by their employer, they must pay the Society for food and rent (a small sum).

I noticed the closeness between the inmates and the supervisor of the hostel. Living practically in one room with them, this man would very likely be able to become aware easily of personal difficulties and, in particular, discern small changes that may betray relapses into the drug habit, such as irregularities in work habits, in intake of food and beverages, or those well-known physical signs of possible drug usage, as watery eyes, drowsiness, paleness, etc.

The Society is now planning to establish a separate hostel for ex-addicts.

The Siu Lam Project

An interesting experiment has been the settlement of former prisoners in Siu Lam Valley, New Territories (Ill. 15). This settlement, which I visited during my first stay, was established under the auspices of the Christian Welfare and Relief Council with the help of a gift from the British Council of Churches and with the cooperation of the Lutheran World Service. Actual labor on the project was provided by inmates of Tai Lam prison, who were told that a number of then-undesignated inmates would benefit from this settlement.

At Siu Lam, a road had been built into a narrow valley where, after a great deal of excavation, four cottages were erected. One of these cottages housed bachelors, while the others were each given to a family along with patches of land, seeds, and some farm animals, such as pigs and poultry. On the premises I met Mr. Si Yi Lee, Executive Secretary of the Hong Kong Christian Welfare and Relief Council, who told me that the small farms by which the former addicts were to make a living for themselves

Illustration 15.
AGRICULTURAL SETTLEMENT OF EX-PRISONERS FROM TAI LAM PRISON AT SIU LAM
VALLEY
(Courtesy, Hong Kong Prisons Department)

and their families were not sufficient for their support. His organization, therefore, was trying to provide the settlers either with home industries or with factory jobs. In the latter case, the men would go to work in factories that were not too far away, while their wives tended the farm.

Aftercare for Voluntary Patients

As we have seen, the Castle Peak Treatment Centre had an almoner with 3 assistants who were in charge of aftercare. Patients are encouraged to see them once a week immediately after discharge. After three months, this is decreased to one visit per month. It often happens in Hong Kong that the former addict, because of his job commitments, cannot visit the aftercare workers. In this case, the patient's wife is asked to see the almoner periodically and report to him in her husband's place.

It was found that the rehabilitation of the patients posed a peculiar problem:

> "A high-class hairdresser may find that he will have to become a barber in a second rate shop and work his way up again. A tailor may have to turn to machine-sewing shirts a few months ... Those that have jobs complain of long hours, insufficient energy for hard labour, and may have sudden impulses to resign." [64]

The Pui Sun Fraternal Association

The medical officers of Castle Peak had suggested, in August 1961, the creation of a club for ex-addicts. In cooperation with the Secretary for Chinese Affairs, a club, the Pui Sun Fraternal Association, was registered in May 1962 — *Pui Sun* meaning "New Life". Its aims are:

> "To provide recreational facilities and organised programmes for ex-drug addicts following their treatment in hospital, with the hope that by group participation, it may promote a better and healthier life, and help them to regain confidence and dignity in becoming normal human beings of the Community, instead of being secluded in disgrace and distress." [65]

The activities of this club comprise social gatherings, discussions, and sports such as swimming, weight-lifting, Chinese shadow boxing and Chinese music (Ill. 16).

The Association has rented a flat of approximately 450 square feet in Kowloon which is open to members from 9 a.m. to 9 p.m. The membership at the time of my second visit comprised approximately 50 "full members" and 100 associate members, the former having received a nalline test, paid an admission fee of H.K. $ 5.— and given a membership card. Associate members pay a monthly subscription of H.K. $ 2.—, but have not been given the nalline test. I asked what would happen to members in case of a relapse. I understand that they would lose their good standing in the Association, but that the doors would not be closed to them. This question has so far not caused problems, it appears, nor has the Association developed into a drug trafficking place —→ something very much feared by many in America for similar organizations.

Illustration 16.

THE PUI SUN FRATERNAL ASSOCIATION
Former addicts and members of their families join in a music group.
(Courtesy, Lutheran World Federation)

The membership fees cover only a fraction of the Association's expenses. The major financial support is offered by the Lutheran World Service, which is now also introducing casework.

A Board of Advisors in which the Almoner's Department, the Hong Kong Medical and Health Department, The Secretary for Chinese Affairs, and the Lutheran World Service are represented, serves the Association.

Other Organizations

A number of other agencies, often church oriented, have provided or are still providing "prison welfare services", i.e., services either to a prisoner or his family before or after discharge. CARITAS and the Salvation Army, specializing in prison "visiting", have already been mentioned. The Salvation Army, in particular, takes care of the women at Lai Chi Kok Prison.

Other voluntary agencies whose names were mentioned to me as being active in work with or for drug addicts were the Hong Kong Christian Welfare and Relief Council, the Presbyterian Case Work Center, and the Catholic Welfare Conference. Some voluntary agencies shy away from drug addicts as, for example, a voluntary organization I visited that was interested in the care of children from needy families. This organization provides children with, among other things, the financial support necessary for their education, but it refuses, as a matter of policy, to accept children of drug addicts for fear that any funds given to the children would be diverted for the purchase of narcotics — a very regrettable situation for the children but nonetheless understandable.

In August 1962, the Lutheran World Service proposed an after-care project for addicts which would serve both ex-prisoners from Tai Lam and ex-patients from the voluntary centers. A small pilot project was started with a carefully selected group of approximately ten to twenty who were helped to find jobs, places to live, and given financial grants until they became self-supporting.[66]

1 *1959 White Paper*, para 32.
2 On October 18, 1961, one of the days on which I visited the institution, the roll call was 742 inmates assembled for muster.
3 Commissioner of Prisons, *Annual Departmental Report 1959/60*, plate facing p. 6; "Hong Kong's Prison for Drug Addicts", *Bulletin on Narcotics*, Vol. 13, No. 1, January—March 1961, pp. 13—30 (especially Figure 2, p. 14).
4 Commissioner of Prisons, *Annual Departmental Report 1960/61*, para. 79. The Tai Lam Prison personnel practice a routine escape drill, which is then used in the rare instances of an actual escape.
5 Hong Kong Prisons, *Standing Orders* No. 556—565 (n.d.).
6 See Chapter III, p. 51.
7 They are, however, unarmed.
8 When, during my stay, I gave a lecture for Chinese students at one of the Hong Kong Colleges, I noticed how difficult it was to get a discussion started with them by comparison to American students. If this is the case with students, think of how much greater the difficulties are in establishing an interchange of ideas with Tai Lam inmates, many of whom have little education, are still suffering from withdrawal symptoms and are too shy to express themselves.
9 "Hong Kong's Prison for Drug Addicts", *op. cit.*, p. 18.
10 Joel Fort, "Narcotics: The International Picture", *California Youth Authority Quarterly*, Vol. 14, No. 2, Summer, 1961, pp. 3—17.

[11] Superintendent of H. M. Prison (Tai Lam), *Report for Period Ending 30th September, 1960* (unpublished). The report stresses that such work is preferable to "so-called occupational therapy in restrictive surroundings".

[12] *Ibid.*

[13] More about this settlement will be below.

[14] The Department of Prisons plans several new open prisons in areas where such aforestation is needed. One of them has opened at Chi Ma Wan on the Island of Lantao (see below).

[15] Commissioner of Prisons, *Annual Departmental Report, 1960/61,* para. 63.

[16] Unpublished report for the quarter, April 1 to July 30, 1961.

[17] *Prison Rules, 1954,* Rule No. 46.

[18] See Commissioner of Prisons, *Annual Departmental Report, 1960/61,* para. 72.

[19] According to unpublished figures supplied through the courtesy of the Prison Administration.

[20] Registrar, Supreme Court, *Annual Departmental Report,* Table IX.

[21] For a brief description of Hong Kong's correctional institutions, see Russell J. Storey, "Courts and Prisons in the Far East", *The Magistrate,* Vol. 18, No. 4, April 1962, pp. 44—46.

[22] Hong Kong Commissioner of Prisons, *Annual Departmental Report, 1960/61,* para. 32.

[23] Storey, *op. cit.,* p. 46.

[24] Commissioner of Prisons, *Annual Departmental Report, 1960/61,* para. 31.

[25] The specially designed open prison at Plover Cove will be erected near a large Government project for converting an inlet of the sea into a fresh-water reservoir. The prisoners will be used a great deal in accessory work for this project, including aforestation.

[26] Commissioner of Prisons, *Annual Departmental Report, 1960/61,* para. 35.

[27] *Ibid.*

[28] For various approaches to this controversy and on the English handling of the narcotics problem, see the following, among other writings: D. J. Cantor, "The Criminal Law and the Narcotics Problem", *Journal of Criminal Law, Criminology and Police Science,* Vol. 51, No. 5, Jan-Feb., 1961, pp. 512—527; W. B. Elridge, *Narcotics and the Law. A Critique of the American Experiment in Narcotic Drug Control* (Chicago, American Bar Foundation, 1957); Joint Committee of the American Bar Association and the American Medical Association, *Drug Addiction. Crime or Disease?* (Bloomington, Ind., Indiana University Press, 1961); G. Larimore and H. Brill, "The British Narcotic System", *New York State Journal of Medicine,* Vol. 60, January 1, 1960, pp. 107—115; A. R. Lindesmith, "The British System of Narcotics Control", *Law and Contemporary Problems,* Vol. 22, Winter, 1957, pp. 138—154; E. M. Schur, *Narcotic Addiction in Britain and America. The Impact of Public Policy* (Bloomington, Ind., Indiana University Press, 1962); U.S. Treasury Department, Advisory Committee to the Federal Bureau of Narcotics, *Comments on Narcotic Drugs: Interim Report of the Joint Committee of the American Bar Association and the American Medical Association on Narcotic Drugs* (Washington, D.C., c. 1958); J. Zusman, "A Brief History of the Narcotics Control Controversy", *Mental Hygiene,* Vol. 45, No. 3,

1961, pp. 383—388.

28a E.g., California. Special Study Commission on Narcotics. *Final Report* (Sacramento, Calif., 1961), p. 101.

29 Interim Report, *Drug Addiction: Crime or Disease?, op. cit.,* p. 132.

30 *Ibid.,* p. 133.

31 United Kingdom, Ministry of Health, Department of Health for Scotland, *Drug Addiction: Report of the Interdepartmental Committee* (London, H.M.S.O., 1961), Section 35. The Committee was headed by Sir Russell Brain.

32 Ploscowe in: Joint Committee of the American Bar Association and the American Medical Association, *op. cit.,* Annex A, p. 78.

33 No. 13 of the *Dangerous Drug Regulations* generally authorized "every duly qualified medical practitioner, and every registered dentist, and every approved veterinary surgeon and every person employed and engaged in dispensing medicine at any public hospital or other public institution, being a person duly registered under the Pharmacy and Poisons Ordinance, or being approved by the director, and every person in charge of a laboratory for purposes of research or instruction attached to the University of Hong Kong, or to any public hospital or other institution approved by the director for the purpose . . . so far as is necessary for the practice of his profession or employment in such capacity to be in possession of a supply of the drugs". And, according to regulation 6(a), "A prescription shall only be given by a registered medical practitioner when required for purposes of medical treatment".

34 Hong Kong Narcotics Advisory Committee, *Progress Report, 1959/60,* para. 28.

35 *Hong Kong 1962,* p. 436, lists 1189 registered and provisionally registered medical practitioners and Government medical officers.

36 See Chapter III, pp. 39—41.

37 *1959 White Paper,* para. 34.

38 *Drug Addicts Treatment and Rehabilitation Ordinance* (No. 34 of 1960), Sections 3, 4 and 6. The superintendent may, however, use any person employed at the institution to carry out his functions.

39 *Ibid.,* Sections 7 and 10.

40 *Ibid.,* Section 12.

41 *Ibid.,* Section 16.

42 *Ibid.*

43 *Ibid.,* Section 18.

44 *Ibid.,* Section 21. The provisions of the *Drug Addicts Treatment and Rehabilitation Regulations, 1960* (Supplement No. 2, *Government Gazette* No. 45, September 9, 1960) deal especially with the features that make the treatment centers closed institutions.

45 Planned to comprise 120 beds; 60 were available at the time of my visit.

46 Secretary of Chinese Affairs, *Annual Departmental Report 1960/61,* para. 19.

46a The word "open" refers here to security conditions.

47 This is based mainly on the Centre's unpublished annual reports for 1961/62 and 1962/63, from which also the following quotations are taken.

48 Only men are taken into the Centre; no facilities exist for women.

49 A. M. Rodrigues, "Chairman's Speech", S.A.R.D.A. *Shek Kwu Chau Centre* .... (Commemorative booklet; Hong Kong, 1963), pp. 8—9.

49a The *Follow Up and Aftercare Report No. 1* of S.A.R.D.A.'s Aftercare Service (February 1964) reports 158 discharges, 12 for misbehavior or bad influence; leaving out 43 too recent cases, there were 11 confirmed and 13 suspected relapses among the remaining 115 (together 21 %). Difficulties in finding employment led to the establishment of the Pui Sun Cleansing Company, formed by ex-addicts to provide cleaning service in large housing estates and jobs for unskilled workers. Another leaflet, *The Process of Intake, Rehabilitation and Discharge of Treated Addicts* (November 1963) establishes a three-stage procedure and changes the designation of patients from "sick man" to "one being rehabilitated".

50 *Hong Kong Tiger Standard,* October, 22, 1962.

51 E.g., between January 1960 and March 1961, the Board considered 1337 cases of whom 5 % (68) were accepted for after-care. Four per cent (54) were still under study at the end of the quarter. There were 91 % (1215) rejections - 84 % (1122) after the first hearing, the remaining 7 % (93) on review.

52 An exception to this are those cases which have to be admitted for aftercare because they live in resettlement areas.

53 Translated by J. K. H.

54 Hong Kong Discharged Prisoners' Aid Society, *Annual General Meeting 1963: Chairman's Report,* p. 3.

55 Hong Kong Discharged Prisoners' Aid Society, *Statistical Report ... during the year 1st April 1961—31st March, 1962 and 1st April, 1962—31st March, 1963.*

56 According to the Society's income and expenditure account, H.K.D.P.A.S. *Quarterly Newsletter,* Jan.—March 1962, p. 1.

57 H.K.D.P.A.S., *Chairman's Report, 1961,* p. 2.

58 *Hong Kong Tiger Standard,* November 1, 1963.

59 H.K.D.P.A.S., *Chief Welfare Officer's Report,* 1 April-30 June 1963, p. 5.

60 *Chairman's Report, 1961,* p. 1. The above figures include both addicted and non-addicted dischargees but not police supervisees.

61 H.K.D.P.A.S., Chairman's Annual Speech, 1962, p. 3.

62 H.K.D.P.A.S., *Chief Welfare Officer's Report,* April 1—June 30, 1963, p. 4.

63 H.K.D.P.A.S., *Chief Welfare Officer's Report,* Dec. 1962, p. 1.

64 Castle Peak Drug Addiction Treatment Centre, *Annual Report 1961/62.*

65 This description is based on a leaflet distributed by Lutheran World Service.

66 Lutheran World Service, *Project for the After-Care of Narcotics Addicts* (1962) and Quarterly Reports.

CHAPTER VI

SUMMARY AND CONCLUDING REMARKS

Chapter I: Introduction

Out of a population of approximately three million and a half, 98 per cent speak Chinese as their usual language and 82 per cent live in urban areas. Only 48 per cent of the inhabitants are born in the Colony; most of the others come from the neighboring Chinese province of Kwangtung.

Hong Kong's economy is based on its free port and on a rapidly growing industrialization. Its employment situation is somewhat irregular because of the overdemand for skilled and certain groups of unskilled workers and the lack of employment for others. There are no restrictions on working hours for male adult workers; many of them work long hours seven days a week.

An especially acute social problem is Hong Kong's population explosion, caused in large part by an enormous influx of refugees from Communist China. Nearly every third person in the Colony is a refugee. The overcrowding resulting from this tremendous population growth has in turn caused both a housing and a water supply shortage. This housing shortage still continues despite energetic measures taken by the Government and private agencies.

Chapter II: Brief History of Drug Addiction in China and Hong Kong

From the T'ang Dynasty on (618—907 A.D.), opium has been used in China for medicinal purposes.

The custom of smoking it may have come from Indonesia. The first Western nation which imported opium for smoking purposes in China may have been Portugal. During the eighteenth century the habit spread, and the British-owned East India Company began importing greater and greater quantities of the drug.

Around 1800, the Chinese Central Government declared the importation of opium illegal, but most authorities on the lower levels ignored this prohibition. Large-scale smuggling, supported by provincial and local officials, began to develop together with a wide cultivation of the poppy in China itself. When the Chinese Government took measures against British merchants at Canton in order to put a stop to the opium trade, the "First Opium War" of 1840 broke out between those nations. China lost this war and had to cede Hong Kong to the British in 1841.

Ever since that time, opium has been important to the Colony. Hong Kong served as a center for the opium trade with both China and, towards the end of the Nineteenth Century, with the United States. Until 1914, the opium business within the Colony was farmed out as a monopoly to the highest bidder, except for some short periods. During the interruptions, and from 1913/14 to World War II, the Hong Kong Government itself operated opium shops.

The first restrictions were promulgated in the 1880's. In 1908, the Colony began greater and greater curtailment of opium import, export, and consumption and, after World War II, completely outlawed them. During the 1950's heroin started to replace opium. In the Walled-City of Kowloon, where, due to an internationally doubtful situation, no sovereignty was exercised and the use of narcotics went unabated until approximately 1959, when the British authorities began to enforce law in the district. In 1959, the Colony initiated a narcotics drive characterized by stricter law enforcement, new legislative measures, and a propaganda campaign. A special prison for narcotics addicts, H.M. Prison (Tai Lam) was opened, followed by the opening of Voluntary Treatment Centres, at Castle Peak early in 1961, and on Shek Kwu Chau Island in 1963.

In this historical study we encountered what appears to have been the first systematic investigation into the physical and psycho-social conditions of drug addicts. It was undertaken by the Rev. George Smith in Amoy, China, around 1846.

The Replacement of Opium by Heroin

The replacement of opium by a drug considered much more dangerous, heroin, upon introduction of anti-opium measures, was a common occurrence not only in Hong Kong but also in Japan, Thailand, and other places. Only too often does one hear in these places that the situation is now "worse than before". Actually, this is nothing new to America. After all, the same happened in the United States, only it happened earlier. It is probably very late at this time, to do something about this dangerous trend because there are very few countries left where opium is still being smoked, but before anti-opium measures are enforced in these last places, perhaps it should be studied very carefully whether the replacement of that drug by heroin could not be avoided by appropriate measures.

Smuggling

Legislation of narcotics in some form or other does not necessarily do away *all* smuggling. Our historical survey has shown that at one time or another both legal opium sales *and* illegal smuggling coexisted in both China and Hong Kong. Indeed, for many years a similar situation prevailed in the United States. It should be considered that smuggling has its own economic laws which have nothing to do with the addiction problem *per se,* but with differences in price levels between countries, by restrictions of available quantities, and so on.

Every day, innumerable goods which can be consumed legally are nonetheless smuggled over many customs borders. Hong Kong, for example, experiences a certain amount of smuggling in alcoholic beverages, yet the Colony has, to my knowledge, no serious alcoholism problem. Rather, the reason for this smuggling is simply that these beverages are cheaper outside the Colony, and especially on the Chinese mainland. Thus, for example, even if in some countries legislation permitting physicians to administer maintenance doses were enacted, it would not necessarily do away with all contraband. However, the continuation of some narcotics smuggling should not necessarily be considered evidence that the enacted legislation is poor. After all, we do not outlaw alcohol, diamonds, or gold merely because there is some smuggling going on in these goods.

At this occasion, I wish to make a plea for further studies of the *history* of drug abuse -- not only in Hong Kong but in the United States as well. Had, e.g., the historical change from opium to heroin in the United States been studied earlier, similar experiences could perhaps have been avoided elsewhere.

Other studies of the history of narcotics may also well yield data which are not only of academic interest but also serve immediate concerns with respect to drug problems.

Nowadays, historical approaches to social problems are perhaps sometimes neglected to a certain degree. In studying drug addiction, we cannot escape the fact that we are dealing so often with "historic" events, — events created by human beings in the dimension of time. Even if the "historical method" of study may not always elicit data that lend themselves easily to generalizations, the systematic and critical study of existing historical documents and their interpretation may lead to important insights. For example, we have not always been able to ascertain sufficiently the actual number of addicts.[1] Has their number really decreased or has it perhaps increased in the course of history? While we probably cannot make up for the lack of existing statistics, historical studies may yield important clues to the answer and may even make it possible to obtain a reasonable picture of the trend in narcotics use in the United States for the last 150 years.

Another question of present-day importance concerns the role played and the results obtained by American narcotics clinics between about 1912 and 1925. To my knowledge, no detailed study of them exists so far. Some claim that these clinics had "failed". Others present evidence to the contrary.[2] Only a historical study will tell.

Chapter III: Present-Day Addiction

S t a t i s t i c s

The number of drug users in Hong Kong is unknown, although earlier estimates set the number somewhere between 150 000 and 250 000. More recently, the number is believed to be considerably smaller, perhaps as low as 50 000, although there have also been estimates of 300 000 and higher.

In the United States, too, the number of drug users is uncertain — estimates range from 45 000 to 1 000 000. Under such circumstances, any comparison between the number of drug users in Hong Kong and the number in the U.S. lacks sufficient basis. Furthermore, although the rural areas in both the U.S. and the Colony are almost entirely free of addiction, over 80 per cent of Hong Kong's population lives in big cities while a much smaller per cent of the United States population is urban. Thus, if a comparison were to be made at all, it would be fairer to compare the number of addicts in Victoria and Kowloon with the number of addicts in comparable American cities rather than with the number in the entire United States.

As with all crime statistics, a direct comparison between the number of narcotics offenders in Hong Kong and America is also not admissible. Differences in law, law enforcement, court practices, and social conditions between the two countries make comparison of such figures impossible — a problem under discussion ever since it was brought up at the General Statistical Congress held in Brussels in 1853. [3]

Further study is recommended as a means of arriving at closer estimates of the true number of addicts in both countries. Techniques for making such studies have already been suggested by the "dark figure" studies undertaken in the field of crime statistics.

Effects of Heroin and Opium

It is widely believed that heroin is more damaging and its effects more difficult to cure than opium since it is the stronger of the two drugs. Actually we know only little about this. For example, with respect to morphine, the White House *Progress Report* just recently stated that, contrary to a widespread conception, that drug does not differ significantly from heroin in its effects,[4] although the two drugs differ in strength.[5] For this reason, a systematic investigation should be made into the differences — pharmaceutical, psychological, and social — in the effects of heroin and opium. A good place for such studies in Hong Kong, where opium is still used relatively frequently.

Narcotics in Mainland China

Opiates used in Hong Kong seem to come primarily from Southeast Asia. Although Communist China's location over the border of the Colony is very conducive to smuggling, that country, it seems, doet not send opiates directly into Hong Kong. The manufacture of heroin partly takes place in Hong Kong and Macau. Recently such manufacturing has also been observed to take place in Thailand and other South East Asia countries.

Opium Seizures

The amounts of opium and opiates seized in Hong Kong vary a great deal, and, while they indicate that the law is being vigorously enforced, they do not necessarily indicate how much narcotics are being consumed.

Trend

If crime rates rather than raw figures are used in the statistical analysis, the number of narcotics offenses committed in Hong Kong during the last few years do not appear alarming. The figures from 1955/56 to 1960/61 vacillate, the main increase in number of narcotics offenses occurred after the narcotics drive started, and after the narcotics laws were broadened. But these increases should be attributed in the first place to the wider coverage of the penal provisions and in the second place to intensified law enforcement rather than to an increase in drug use.

This trend, then, seems to indicate that the Colony is keeping its addiction problem under reasonable control, and this despite numerous difficulties and extreme social problems.

Users and Traffickers

The so-called "triad" societies, secret societies surrounded by an elaborate ritual, have in the past controlled, to a certain extent, the narcotics traffic in Hong Kong. Less formally structured and ritual-oriented groups, however, seem to have gained more prominence lately in local trafficking.

It would not be realistic to expect that much could be done at the present time with respect to a sociological study, formal or informal, of these groups. But the study of the characteristics of the different persons connected with narcotics — traffickers, peddlers, addict-peddlers, and users as they come to the attention of the authorities — may be developed greatly.

Imprisonment of Addicts

As we have seen, two out of three Hong Kong prison inmates are narcotics users. Large percentages of addicts can also be found among the prisoners in the institutions of some of the American jurisdictions. Large numbers of drug users in prison populations need particular consideration because of the only all too well-known overcrowding of insitutions, as it exists frequently both in America and Hong Kong. Large-scale and long imprisonment for narcotics offenses naturally contributes greatly to overcrowding and, as experience shows, even often brings it to a point where rehabilitative work — not only for addicts, but for *all* inmates — becomes very difficult.

In this connection, the following figures are of interest: [6]

England and Wales	65 persons imprisoned		per 100 000 of the
Japan	89 ,,	,,	civilian population
United States	178 ,,	,,	

In presenting these figures, Mr. James V. Bennett, the Director of the U.S. Bureau of Prisons, severely criticized the United States for putting so many persons behind bars, as compared with the other countries and urged a reduction. How do Hong Kong's figures compare with those cited above? In 1960/61 Hong Kong's daily average prison population amounted to 5 678 inmates. With a general population of 3 128 000 as per March 1961, the corresponding rate is 181 per 100 000 inhabitants,[7] that is practically the same as the very high United States rate.

Whenever drug offenders constitute a high percentage of the prison population, the question may be raised whether imprisonment is really the best way of dealing with them. Nobody will doubt the necessity of severity against traffickers, but it is doubtful whether imprisonment is the most effective way of dealing with the addict, and even with the small-scale addict pusher who constitute the bulk of the narcotics offenders in the institutions. New legislation and changes in administrative practices may be worth while considering, and legislators may often be convinced to look favorably at such changes not only when

human values are preserved when locking-up is avoided but also at
financial aspects: imprisonment is indeed often very costly when compared with other means of treatment.

Characteristics of Addicts

Our study of the characteristics of drug users in both prisons showed a
large number to be in their early thirties. Relatively few were younger
than that, although most had become drug users before the age of 30.
All together, two-thirds had started the habit up to age 35; about 10 per
cent had begun in their early teens.

Only about one-fifth to one-fourth of the inmates had been addicted
for less than five years; the average length of addiction was from 10 to
14 years.

According to the addicts' statements, the amount spent daily on drugs
keeps increasing with the length of drug use until a certain point when
the amount spent begins to decrease. Tai Lam addicts came from primarily low economic groups, but very few are listed as jobless. The younger
addicts seem to be more highly skilled than the older ones. Over one-
fourth of the addicts investigated had had one year or less of education.
A comparison of addicts who had had nine years or more of school with
those who had had one year or less shows that the few drug abusers who
had had higher-status occupations were members of the well educated
groups, but, otherwise, there is little difference in the occupational status
of the less educated addicts — especially with respect to the percentages
of skilled and unskilled workers. Concerning the reasons given for drug
use, there is also no great difference between those who had received a
relatively good deal of schooling and those who had received little. Over
50 per cent in both categories claimed they took narcotics as a medication
against disease. A breakdown by age shows that those 30 years old or less
claimed medical reasons in only 45 per cent of the cases, while those
above that age claimed them in about $66^2/_3$ per cent of the cases. There
is practically no distinction between the group aged 31 to 55 and the
group aged 56 and over as far as the proportion of those claiming medical
reasons is concerned.

A breakdown of all known offenses committed by inmates of our group
from Victoria prison shows a total of 64 per cent narcotics offenses and

36 per cent non-narcotics offenses. In 94 per cent of the cases, offenders were sentenced to less than one year of imprisonment. Only 18 per cent of the prisoners had committed no previous offenses. A comparison of first-known and last offenses of the inmates showed that 66 per cent of the first-known offenses and 88 per cent of last offenses were narcotics offenses. This seems to indicate a pattern of specialization in drug crimes on the part of the drug offender.

Those using heroin exclusively were, in general, fairly young, those who used opium exclusively were older. Contrary to a popular belief, exclusive users of heroin spent more on their drug than did those who used only opium. A relatively high percentage of seamen was found among the small number who administered narcotics intravenously.

Female and juvenile addicts are rare in the Colony, though women and children not infrequently carry narcotics. Hong Kong's low rates of drug use by minors and juvenile delinquency may be contrasted with America's high rates. It has been claimed that juvenile delinquency and drug abuse in America's slums both result to a great extent from the young person's withdrawal from the generally accepted values of the community because of Society's failure to give him the opportunities it had promised.[8] Hong Kong's slum youth is probably much worse off materially and is given fewer opportunities for "moving up" and obtaining the "good things in life" than his American counterpart. However, it is quite possible that he has fewer aspirations. An American child, who learns that he may reach the highest goals because everybody is entitled to equal opportunities, grows up with great expectations. The underprivileged often discovers these opportunities are denied him for no fault of his own. It is quite conceivable that such aspirations are not nurtured in the Colony's underprivileged youth. Thus despite lower living standards and fewer changes for improvement, frustrations are perhaps felt less strongly and do not lead to similar endeavors to obtain illegally, what youngsters in American slums believe should be theirs legally, nor to acting out frustrations through violence, nor to escaping from discouragement through drug abuse. This speculation is offered as a suggestion for further exploration.

One of the most pressing unanswered questions, especially for the Hong Kong addict is, why only some persons become addicted if everyone is living under apparently the same hardships, or what "enables the vast-majority to resist drug abuse"? [9]

Chapter IV. Preventive Measures in Hong Kong

Preventive Measures

A number of general social measures are being undertaken in Hong Kong, which, while not aimed directly at the drug abuser, may, by the general improvements they bring about, have a limited preventive effect on narcotics offenders. Through the resettlement program initiated by Government and private parties, large numbers of squatters, street sleepers, roof-dwellers are provided with housing in big "developments". Although drug addiction may be considered as sufficient grounds for eviction from these settlements, this is not enforced in the case of releasees from Tai Lam who are receiving aftercare.

Another program, the establishment of a large number of medical outpatient centers, which treat patients without means free of charge, may have some preventive effect in view of the addict's generally poor state of health and the Chinese custom of using narcotics as a form of self-medication. Through these centers the services of Western-style physicians are made available to the population, who appear to be turning more and more to modern medicine for curing their ailments.

Law enforcement is the main preventive measure used by Hong Kong against narcotics abuse. It is the job of the Preventive Service, which controls smuggling into and out of the Colony, and of the Police, which deals with drug problems within the Colony. Both have well-organized and efficient specialized narcotics units. International cooperation is practiced on a wide scale. The courts maintain jurisdiction over narcotics offenses according to the provisions of the *Dangerous Drugs Ordinance* and subsidiary legislation. Compared with the United States, penalties of imprisonment have generally been much shorter but there seems to be a trend towards inflicting heavier penalties, especially for such offenses as the illegal manufacturing of heroin.

Deterrence

Far away from following the non-punitive British approach, Hong

Kong's efforts to fight the narcotics problem through criminal legislation resemble more those of the United States, even if the penalties involved have not yet reached that degree of severity which often exists in the United States. There should be little illusion about long penalties having a significant effect of "general" deterrence. It is an old, popular myth that by writing a harsh punishment into the law, a deterrent effect would be obtained. To be sure, such threats may deter certain potential offenders, but this applies hardly to addicts who act under strong craving, and it is also generally recognized, that deterrence depends in the first place on effective law *enforcement*, and not on mere legal threats of punishment.[10] In other words, a person does not get scared away easily from the thought of heavy penalties if there is little chance that he may get caught, but he may be discouraged from committing a criminal act if he can be reasonably sure that he is to be punished, even if the punishment is a relatively light one. Law enforcement can hardly supply such a guarantee in spite of much devoted work and of spectacular success in particular cases by the services in charge. In comparison to the opiates actually consumed illegally, law enforcement efforts only too often appear like a drop in the bucket; apart from occasional harrassments through raids and so forth, narcotics remain easily accessible through the years both in New York's East Harlem and Hong Kong's Wan Chai. And if the laws cannot be enforced adequately, legal threats too will not make much impact.

Propaganda and Public Opinion

Since November, 1959, the Hong Kong Government, in cooperation with private organizations, has undertaken a wide-scale propaganda campaign in an effort to educate the public on the dangers of drug abuse. Practically all types of publicity have been used in the Government's campaign posters and leaflets in particular. Moreover, special attention has been given to indoctrinating the civil servants of the Colony.

In establishing any similar anti-narcotics propaganda campaign in countries such as the United States, a combined action-research program might be useful as a means of measuring the effects of deterrent devices. I am inclined to believe that — at least in America — the presentation of the dangers of narcotics in matter-of-fact style is preferable to excessively frightening pictures and texts. The latter helps reaffirm the misleading and already too popular image of the hopeless "dope fiend," an image which has led to a good deal of overly punitive and extremely unsound correctional legislation. Furthermore, such propaganda only aggravates the addict's feeling of worthlessness and hopelessness, creating more psychological obstacles to his rehabilitation. After withdrawal, he is often extremely reluctant to enter the long process of social rehabilitation (which he does not understand), and is more inclined to agree with the popularly held belief: "Once a junkie, always a junkie."

Thus, a well balanced campaign should publicize the addict's need for treatment as well as carefully worded warnings.

To my knowledge, no survey has as yet been made in Hong Kong on what various population groups — especially the addicts and those strata from which most addicts come — think about the narcotics problem. A survey of this kind, using public opinion research methods, would not only be most interesting as an evaluation of current opinion but may also help in the formulation of measures against the use of narcotics.

Chapter V: Treatment of Drug Addiction

Correctional Treatment

So long as voluntary treatment facilities are not yet sufficiently available, those treatment facilities which exist within the Colony's correctional system are particularly important. Indeed, the Hong Kong Government regards imprisonment of the addict as an opportunity to cure him.

H. M. Prison (Tai Lam), located in the New Territories, is a very efficiently run institution for over 700 drug addicts. About one-fourth of the Colony's addict prisoners are sent there. Security measures at Tai Lam are minimal. According to the intake policy, persons with a short history of drug abuses are preferred to those with a longer one. Members of secret societies, known gangsters, and persons with long criminal records are not eligible for Tai Lam. The discipline is basically authoritarian.

In view of the ethnic and socio-cultural differences, correctional views and approaches in Hong Kong may, of course differ from those in the United States. To be sure, authoritarian approaches similar to those at Tai Lam prison also exist in some of the more traditional correctional systems elsewhere. Then, too, many believe that narcotics addicts have to be handled with a certain amount of authority. On the whole, however, the view generally held in the United States is that a very authoritarian correctional system — though it facilitates the efficient operation of the institution — presents the inmate with a situation so unrelated to daily living that it fails to develop in him the very qualities, especially initiative and responsibility, he will eventually need for his rehabilitation. Certain types of authority also do not encourage continuous staff observation of the inmates' individual treatment needs, and are not conducive to the establishment of a *rapport* between, or "therapeutic community" of, staff and inmates. Instead, as far as conditions in the United States are concerned, the drawing of too strict a line between these two groups may push prisoners into the "inmate society", a highly undesirable subculture usually dominated by the worst of the lot who, by imposing their anti-social values on the rest of the inmates, kill most attempts at rehabilitation.

Despite these objections, a certain degree of individualized observation of the prisoner at Tai Lam takes place in his contacts with the prison physician and, more recently through the establishment of a service of rehabilitation workers who interview prisoners, and members of their families. This service, however, is still limited because of budget reasons and because of the Prison Administration's difficulties in finding a sufficient number of suitable social workers.

The treatment program at Tai Lam is aimed mainly at the inmate's physical rehabilitation — withdrawal (which actually takes place before he comes to Tai Lam), gaining weight, rebuilding good health and physical strength — a program that seems very plausible in view of the fact that drug abuse in Hong Kong is, to a large extent, connected with self-medication for serious diseases such as tuberculosis. Needless to say, this type of program would hardly suffice in dealing with some of the psychological and sociological problems which are being discussed for American addicts, such as their lacking maturation, self-destructive tendencies, homosexuality, the possible existence of a "retreatist" subculture, and so forth.

At Tai Lam, outdoor work, especially on public improvement projects is also considered part of the addict's "rehabilitative training". While no vocational training is provided as such, on-the-job training is given incidentally in such fields as carpentry and masonry. Disabled and older inmates do light work, unless they require hospitalization. All prisoners — even those who are hospitalized — receive a small salary.

This remuneration for all inmates shows that Hong Kong is far ahead of most American institutions, where inmates still do not receive pay. Outdoor work for the public good is a very feasible way of keeping addicts occupied. If the United States were faced with a similar situation and if prisoners here were given this type of work as a means of instilling them with a feeling of being useful, it might be pertinent to evaluate the results of this kind of treatment program. As was the case with most of those studied, addicts who had been uprooted from their native land and who perhaps had not yet developed civic pride in their new place of residence could not always be expected to fully appreciate the civic significance of their labors — especially since most of the projects undertaken at Tai Lam are rural and thus somewhat divorced from the lives most of the addicts had been leading in city slums.

The problem of vocational training is, no doubt, of less importance in Hong Kong than in the United States because there an older inmate population must be dealt with. Trying to institute a program of reforestation in the United States similar to that at Tai Lam might lead to the criticism that outdoor work does not really prepare the addict for the urban employment he may have to find upon release. If feasible, it might be an interesting experiment to offer those ex-addicts, who had been engaged in reforestation at Tai Lam, similar jobs upon their release. Such occupations — which perhaps could be realized with the help of voluntary organizations — would also serve as a means of keeping these men away from their former environment of slums and from access to narcotics. In addition, it might be worth considering to keep a close watch on the current labor market so that inmates could be trained in the type of work in demand after their release, especially in skills needed for newly established industries.

Parole

Hong Kong has no parole system, but each prisoner receives time off for good behavior. This time is computed at the beginning of his penalty and is abrogated only in exceptional cases. Some Hong Kong officials to whom I mentioned parole had an image of it as riddled by corrupt practices, political influence, and favoritism and stressed that their "good-time-off" system was much superior because the prisoner "knows exactly what he can expect." Although parole practices outside of Hong Kong are, to be sure, not always what they should be, we do know that parole can be a successful tool in the rehabilitation of American prisoners — when it is handled effectively and without the drawbacks described above. For example, the experiences of the Diskind program in New York State show how a parole system can work to the addict's benefit.[11] It has been a general experience in most countries that good behavior in an authoritarian prison setting is not always a reliable indication of an addict's potential for successful adjustment to society.

Evaluation

Relatively few statistical data are available on the results obtained with addicts treated at Tai Lam. So far, it seems that about a third of the inmates released resumed the habit and were reconvicted. Needless to say, observers will be most interested in any future evaluations of the results of the Tai Lam treatment program, especially if they could be compared with those of suitable control groups. Doubts may be raised about using drug offense reconviction rates as indicators of an addict's improvement. Although a full cure may not always be accomplished by treatment, there may be ameliorations in spite of relapses in a person's subsequent narcotics use and social behavior. Such ameliorations remain unnoticed if reconviction rates serve as the sole criterion for measuring the success of the treatment. Indeed observers even claim that relapses are unavoidable in certain cases, so that any measurement of success should also take into consideration "lesser" indications of rehabilitation. Among these indications of improvements that have been mentioned as suitable for consideration with American addicts are the gradual extension of the length of time between relapses and signs of better adjustment to daily life, such as improved ability to hold gainful employment.

Other Treatment Institutions

Among other institutions visited were Stanley and Chi Ma Wan prisons, both used — though not exclusively — for drug-using offenders not sent to Tai Lam or Lai Chi Kok, the women's prison in the Colony. With the exception of some difficulties, experienced mainly at the maximum-security at Stanley, the Prison Administration has relatively little trouble with smuggling of narcotics. On the one hand, the rare occurrence of contraband in narcotics is, if my impression is correct, characteristic of several addiction treatment centers in Asia and the Far East, while, on the other hand, the smuggling of drugs into institutions is sometimes considered a more serious problem in the United States. A comparative study of institutions in the East and in America may be suggested. Is there really a significant difference between East and West? If so, is the absence of smuggling related to the "health-oriented" atmosphere of Eastern institutions?

Voluntary Treatment

The British Approach and Hong Kong

Hong Kong is sometimes cited in the American controversy on narcotics as evidence that the British approach does not work in a situation with a large number of addicts. As we have seen, the main difference between the British and the American approach lies in the fact that the British physicians may, under certain strict provisions, administer maintenance doses to addicts, especially if prolonged cures have failed and if the addict appears "incurable" but seems to be able to lead a useful and relatively normal life if he receives drugs in minimum quantities. These British recommendations do not automatically apply to Hong Kong nor have they been set in force there expressly. However, the Hong Kong Dangerous Drugs legislation does give special drug privileges to physicians and related professions. It always exempts from its penal prohibitions those cases where doctors, dentists or veterinarians have prescribed or administered narcotics within their legitimate professional practice. As to the question, what constitutes legitimate medical practice, it has never specifically been decided for Hong Kong, whether the above mentioned case of giving maintenance doses to "incurable" addicts, *bona fide* and under similar safeguards as given in British recommendations (e.g. prolonged attempts at curing, consultation of a second physician), falls within professional ethics. In such a case, and if it ever would come up the decision would be made by a gremium of Hong Kong medical practitioners. It is remarkable that, despite the existence of a presumingly large addict population and despite the physicians' relative freedom in the matter, abuses seem to be low, and, if they occur, they are dealt with not by the criminal courts, but dealt with rather lightly by the public health authorities who keep strict controls on prescribing and administering narcotics. In cases of abuse by physicians, the penalties are admonition or withdrawing the privilege of prescribing or administering dangerous drugs for a few months. In America, the main argument advanced against permitting physicians to administer narcotics to addicts — in carefully selected cases and under equally strict safeguards as in England — has been that the physicians might, in effect, take over the function of the trafficker by prescribing or administering drugs indiscriminately. However, this argument is not borne out by the facts as shown in Hong Kong. In my opinion, it is the integrity of the medical profession that matters for the decision on what privileges physicians should have with respect to narcotics, and not the high or low incidence of addiction. Should we really say that the American physician is so much less trustworthy than his colleagues in Hong Kong and Great Britain?

Voluntary Treatment Centers

In September, 1960, Hong Kong issued the *Drug Addict Treatment and Rehabilitation Ordinance, 1960,* which opened the way for the establishment of voluntary treatment centers. According to one provision in this Ordinance, a patient applying for voluntary treatment must sign a legally binding obligation to remain at the center and to be detained against his will for six months.

In the United States, the difficulties encountered by hospitals for voluntary treatment of narcotics addiction are well-known; all too frequently self-committed patients leave the institution too early and against medical advice, and the institution cannot hold them. The Hong Kong procedure of having voluntary patients sign a similar "binder" appears to be useful, at least in some of the American jurisdictions.

The first such center was opened as a pilot project at Castle Peak in the New Territories in March, 1961, in the newly constructed psychiatric hospital. The Centre has 60 beds. After an initial period of random intake, which lasted only a short time, a policy of a highly selective intake was decided upon. Since then, the Centre has followed this policy. It especially avoids accepting any patient who applies for admission under the pressure of Courts or other authorities. Castle Peak is also an active center for research on psychological, sociological and pharmacological aspects of narcotics addiction and its treatment.

A second treatment center was made available in June, 1963, on the island of Shek Kwu Chau starting with a small group of patients, which was to be raised to the Centre's capacity of 250 patients. The patients are treated in both centers: they first go to Castle Peak where they undergo withdrawal treatment and treatment for any physical diseases they may have. After approximately one month, they continue to Shek Kwu Chau where occupational therapy, together with counseling, individually or in groups, is provided as treatment. As the time approaches for release, the patient is given a home leave. After returning from that leave, he has to take a nalline test. If no signs of drug use are evidenced, he is released and placed under aftercare.

Aftercare

Aftercare for ex-addicts — whether they come out of prison or from voluntary treatment institutions — is considered of greatest importance by all government agencies and private organizations concerned. After-care workers, however, are difficult to recruit in Hong Kong. In order to alleviate the shortage, local institutions of higher learning are now providing special training in social work on the undergraduate level. Aftercare work in Hong Kong has many difficulties which do not exist in other places, mainly because of the fact that so many clients have no fixed address, live as squatters, etc., or cannot always be expected to report because of long working hours.

At the present time, aftercare services in Hong Kong are kept separate for prisoners released from the prisons and for patients from the voluntary treatment centers. For both, aftercare is administered either by the institutions' own aftercare workers or by private organizations.

The Prison Department accepts only a limited number of cases for aftercare service in order to avoid overtaxing the case load of its workers. The selection is made after the Board of Aftercare interviews each prisoner, who must formally declare that he will accept aftercare before he can even be considered by the Board. As the Colony does not have a parole system whereby it has jurisdiction over released prisoners, this service is entirely voluntary. The main reason for the rejection of a candidate is his lack of a fixed address. The Board selects only those who have the best prospects for social rehabilitation, although it *always* accepts prisoners who are tenants in a resettlement project in order to keep them and their families from being evicted. About 6 per cent of the former inmates of Tai Lam — the only institution where this service is available for former addicts — have received the Prison Department's aftercare. The Discharged Prisoners' Aid Society supplements the Prison Department's aftercare services by offering its employment services and hostels to former inmates of Tai Lam Prison, even to those without a fixed abode who are, therefore, ineligible for aftercare by the Prison Department. Each hostel houses about 20 former addicts and is located near sections of town where jobs are available. Close supervision by an experienced house father permits early spotting of relapses.

Various other experiments in the care of former addicts prisoners have been undertaken in Hong Kong, among them a rural settlement for Tai Lam Prison ex-inmates in Siu Lam Valley in the New Territories; these are sponsored by various Church organizations in cooperation with the Government.

Also, the voluntary treatment centers provide aftercare services through their social workers, almoners of the Psychiatric Center in Hong Kong, and private efforts. For former addicts who have come to voluntary centers is the recently established Pui Sun Association, a fraternal organization which undertakes mainly recreational activities.

It was the purpose of this report to describe the drug situation in the Colony for the benefit of those in America and elsewhere who may wish to know more about Hong Kong's long experience with narcotics, perhaps with a view to making use of certain aspects of this experience in their own countries. This description had to be based on observations during relatively short stays and on what source material was available. In view of this, the author hopes that the report may be considered as a stimulant to further investigation.

1 Interesting estimates for the period of approximately 1915—1920 may be found in L. Kolb, and A. G. Du Mez, *The Prevalence and Trend of Drug Addiction in the United States and Factors Influencing It* (Washington, Government Printing Office, 1924). Unfortunately, similar studies do not exist for other periods to my knowledge.

2 On this controversy, see E. M. Schnur, *Narcotics Addiction in Britain and America* (Bloomington, Indiana, University Press, 1962), pp. 63—66.

3 For a discussion of the subject, see United Nations, *Criminal Statistics; Standard Classification of Offences* (1959; U.N. Document No. E/CN.5/337).

4 White House *Ad Hoc* Panel on Drug Abuse, *Progress Report* (Washington, D.C., 1962), pp. 2, 22.

5 United Nations Commission on Narcotic Drugs, *Report of the Sixteenth Session* (24 April—10 May 1961), para. 86. (U.N. Document No. E/3512—E/CN.7/411).

6 J. V. Bennett, Correctional Problems the Court Can Help Solve, *Crime and Delinquency*, Vol. 7, No. 1, Jan. 1961, pp. 1—8.

7 Commissioner of Prisons, *Annual Departmental Report, 1960—61*, paras. 40—41.

8 R. A. Cloward and L. E. Ohlin, *Delinquency and Opportunity: A Theory of Delinquent Gangs* (New York, Free Press of Glencoe), 1960.

9 White House *Ad Hoc* Panel on Drug Abuse, *Progress Report* (Washington, D.C., 1962), p. 56.

10 S. Rubin, *Crime and Juvenile Delinquency*, 2nd ed., (New York and London, Oceana, etc., 1961), p. 129.

11 New York State Division of Parole, *An Experiment in the Supervision of Paroled Offenders Addicted to Narcotic Drugs. Final Report of the Special Narcotic Project.* (Prepared by M. H. Diskind, R. F. Hallinan and J. M. Stanton; c. 1960).

APPENDIX A

English translations of three "Handouts" (Leaflets) distributed among the Hong Kong population during the anti-narcotics campaign of 1960

I

Illustrated Front Cover (See Ill. 11)
"ADDICTION MEANS DEATH"

Contents

Opium, "Red Pills", "White Powder" - will destroy your life:
They are definitely -
* NOT a cure for T.B. or any other disease;
* NOT an aphrodisiac;
* NOT a source of energy;
* NOT to be "tried", lest you will be trapped.

Addicts will -
* become feeble, fragile and decrepit;
* easily fall victims to disease;
* lose their money and employment;
* sink further and further down the social ladder;
* lose their self-respect;
* resort to crime and suffer the consequences;
* inflict misery and suffering upon their wives and children and break up their homes.

Government is doing everything possible -
* to arrest the drug smugglers, traffickers & manufacturers;
* to clean up the divans and drug factories.

Play your part as a good citizen by -
* co-operating with Government;
* not being tempted into the vice of smoking.

If you have any suggestions to combat this evil or require any personal advise concerning narcotics, please contact -

The Secretary for Chinese Affairs (Narcotics Section), Fire Brigade Building - Tel. 33449.

If you have information about divans, traffickers, etc., please contact -

(I) The Hong Kong Police Narcotics Bureau, Room 212,

No. 9, Ice House Street, 2nd floor, Tel. 34347.

„ 34522 Ext. 393.

„ 34522 Ext. 246.

(II) Any Police Station, or

(III) Write to P.O. Box No. 112, Hong Kong.

If you have any information about smuggling, please contact -

The Hong Kong Preventive Service,

Fire Brigade Building - Tel. 32551.

or

The Hong Kong Police Narcotics Bureau.

Both enquiries and information will be treated as confidential.

2

Illustrated Front Cover

"WIPE OUT OPIUM DIVANS AND ALL FACTORIES WHERE NARCOTICS AND DRUGS ARE MANUFACTURED"

Contents

Narcotics peddlars are public enemies -

Hoodlums and undesirables congregate in dark and dingy opium dens, menace to the neighborhood, disturbance to public security. Let us all rise up to wipe them out, in order to preserve law and order.

Narcotics are manufactured scientifically -

Behind closed doors and windows, causing fire hazards; producing all sorts of vices. Let us all cooperate to eliminate this source of the crime.

The Government is launching an all-out effort -

To eradicate all opium dens and narcotics factories; and to arrest drug traffickers and manufacturers alike.

Do your part as good citizens in cooperating with the Government in the anti-narcotics campaign -

Please report to the authorities if you have information about divans, traffickers, etc. You will receive a reward and your information will be treated as confidential.

Procedure of payment of rewards -

The sum of $ 250 or above is to be paid directly by Senior Police Officers. If the informant wishes, rewards below $ 250 will also be paid through Senior Police Officers. Particulars about the informant will be kept confidential. Time and place of meeting may be decided by informant.

Wake up you operators of opium dens and manufacturers of narcotics -

Once you are caught and put behind prison bars, your families will also be involved. So let your conscience be stirred before it is too late.

Special notice to travellers and tourists -

Beware of carrying parcels and packages for others which may contain drugs. When discovered by the police you will be punished accordingly.

If you have any suggestions etc. (as above under 1)

(Translated by L.K.K. and J.K.K.H.)

3

Illustrated Front Cover

"DRUG TRAFFICKERS ARE BLOOD-SUCKING FIENDS"

Contents

Drug traffickers and pedlars are public enemies -

(1) They are instrumental in enticing people to be addicts, thereby shattering their homes and future, and converting them into criminals and depraved beings.
(2) They cheat innocent people and are heartless and unscrupulous. They ruin other people's lives so as to benefit themselves. They violate all rules of heaven and propriety.
(3) They endanger society, and their crimes are extremely serious.

Let us join forces together to eliminate these public enemies.

Government is doing everything possible -

to arrest drug smugglers, traffickers and pedlars;
to clean up the divans and drug factories.

Protect your homes and society by -

co-operating with Government;
informing on drug smugglers, traffickers, pedlars, divans and drug factories.

Substantial rewards will be paid by Government for information leading to the seizure of illegal drugs -

If the reward money amounts to $ 250 or more, it will always be paid by senior officers.
If it is less than $ 250 and if the informant so desires, payment through senior officers can also be arranged. The identity of the informer will be protected. Contact with the informant, the place and the time of meeting, etc. will be arranged in accordance with his own wishes.

Don't be a pedlar

You will be left in the lurch by your gang or your boss when you are caught.
You risk yourself and your family to make money for others.
You wreck people's lives by peddling drugs.
Have a conscience. Why live on others' sufferings?

Be careful when you are asked to carry packages or suitcases for other persons, especially strangers -

Drugs may be hidden therein, and you will become the traffickers' scapegoat.

If you have any suggestions etc. (as above under 1)

APPENDIX B

English text of a leaflet (printed in Chinese and English) by the Secretary for Chinese Affairs. Distributed in 1960 among Hong Kong civil servants

Front Cover

ANTI-NARCOTICS CAMPAIGN
S.C.A.'S APPEAL TO EVERY GOVERNMENT SERVANT FOR HELP

Contents

As you know, Government started an all-out anti-narcotics campaign in November last year with the publication, in both English and Chinese, of a White Paper on the Problem of Narcotic Drugs in Hong Kong. I hope you have been able to find time to read this Paper which outlines both the problem and the measures Government has taken to suppress drug addiction and trafficking, and which at the same time appeals to you and to everyone in Hong Kong for support in a sustained drive against narcotics.

Government has entrusted me with the co-ordination of general policy in the war against narcotics. It is in this capacity that I am addressing you, not only to offer some further general information on the subject, and to expose the alarming consequences of taking dangerous drugs, but also to appeal to you especially, as a responsible citizen and public servant to participate actively in this drive against a vice which is the cause of all manner of harms.

It is well known that once a person starts taking dangerous drugs, there will be no stopping for him. No matter how much he may later repent and bitterly reproach himself for his weakness in giving way, he cannot *of his own accord* rid himself of the habit. There is only one sure way of stopping drug addiction and that is not to start it in the first place. As tens of thousands of people have discovered to their cost, there is no such thing as self-control in any drug addict.

The main reasons why people take to dangerous drugs are the belief that:

It can cure illness or relieve pain;

It will produce a sense of well-being and pleasure or promote sexual strength;

It is a daring thing to do, with a lure of novelty and excitement.

But are these beliefs true? I can assure you that they are not. On taking opium (and even more so heroin), there may be a sensation of pleasant relaxation, ease and warmth. All worries may seem to vanish and the individual can sit and dream, without bothering about responsibilities, money, his job or anything else in the world. All these are illusions of the mind. In the meantime, what is happening to the body? After taking the drug, there is a period of lassitude and then a profound sleep. The body is immobilised and the sleeper is very hard to waken. His face is flushed, the heart slows down, the pulse becomes weaker and the body covered with clammy perspiration. On finally waking, he feels fatigued as though he has been making a violent physical effort. His arms and legs feel heavy. His face will be pale with livid lips, dropped lower jaws, and pinpoint pupils with reddened eyes. His sleep will not have refreshed him. On the contrary, he will feel tired and confused, with a headache. There may be fits of nausea and vomiting. His mouth will be dry and bitter, and his eyes also dry. He will be wholly incapable of any muscular effort.

If dangerous drugs like opium and heroin are taken over a prolonged period, they lead to the derangement of appetite and digestion, disturbance of sleep, vomiting, constipation, emaciation, impotence, and premature old age. All drug addicts are afflicted with constipation.

I am telling you these details because it is important that everyone should clearly realise what are the dread effects of these drugs:

Drugs do not cure disease. Only proper medical treatment can do that.

The sensations of pleasure and well-being occur only in the earliest stages after taking the drug. But what of the horrible physical feelings on waking up? What about the subsequent mental feeling of dejection and remorse? As for promoting sexual strength, these drugs lead in fact to impotence.

It may be a novelty to indulge in drugs, but it is not common sense, for drugs lead to weakening of the body and its resistance to disease and thus an early death.

The next point to emphasize is that taking dangerous drugs is not like taking ordinary food and drink. After a period of drug taking, the pleasurable sensations are not repeated unless the dose is increased. In other words, more and more of the drug is needed in order to satisfy the craving. This particularly applies to heroin which leads to addiction far more quickly than opium. An addict is someone who has taken a drug so often that it has led to an over-powering desire to continue the practice. If he is deprived of the drug, he suffers mental excitement, restlessness, yawning, sneezing, excessive salivation, malaise, palpitation of the heart, cramps, vomiting, diarrhea, pains in the stomach and a burning sensation in the back. The addict is forced to go on taking the drug. Having lost all proper control of himself, he will stoop to any lengths to obtain the drug.

The persons who illegally import dangerous drugs into Hong Kong do so because there is a considerable profit to be made from it. Since this trafficking is dangerous, they charge high prices. To pay these prices, the drug addict will spend all his money. He will neglect his family and relatives, however much he loves them. He will let them starve rather than be deprived of the expensive drugs. If he doesn't have the money, he will beg or borrow it, without the slightest hope or intention of ever paying it back. Failing that, he will steal, lie or do any immoral act to obtain the drug. He is no longer master of himself. He will be useless at his job. His family will despise him. He will cease to pay any attention to his dress, cleanliness or appearance. His pale, greenish and bloodless complexion will show everyone what he is, together with shining eyes, drooping shoulders and a complete lack of all energy.

I have explained enough to show you that, once in the grip of the drug, the addict becomes a slave. There is nothing which he personally can do to cure addiction. An early death is the only release. Once a person begins taking drugs, then nine times out of ten he will go on, in which case he becomes an addict. The distance between a few experimental attempts at drug-taking and addiction is very short indeed, and it is even shorter with heroin which is roughly six to ten times more powerful than opium in its effects.

I hope that I have now made the position clear to you so that you will be able to play your part in advising and discouraging others whose resistance seems to you to be wavering. Tell them why taking dangerous drugs:

does NOT cure illness;
does NOT produce a lasting sense of pleasure;
is NOT a daring thing to do; it is the act of a fool.

Why give one's money to the drug traffickers when it would be better spent on everyday things for one's family and oneself? It is a serious criminal offence to possess dangerous drugs or to take them, and Government takes a serious view of any person committing an offence against the Dangerous Drugs Ordinance.

For the sake of humanity in general, and the welfare of Hong Kong in particular, I sincerely appeal to you to make sure that you fully appreciate and publicize the dangers of drug addiction, and whenever and wherever you can, to participate in the crusade against this vice.

If you want to know anything more, or have any advice or suggestions to offer, please get in touch with the Narcotics Officer in your Department or with Mr. Walter Yeung, Asst. S.C.A. (telephone 28802).

J. C. McDouall,
Secretary for Chinese Affairs

BIBLIOGRAPHY *

Bennett, J. V. "Correctional Problems the Court Can Help Solve", *Crime and Delinquency*, Vol. 7, No. 1 (Jan. 1961), pp. 1—8.

Boal, S. "Hong Kong: Its Many Splendored Face", *Diners' Club Magazine*, Vol. 14, No. 8 (Oct. 1963), pp. 28—35, 40.

California Special Study Commission on Narcotics. *Final Report* (Sacramento, Calif., 1961).

Cantor, D. J. "The Criminal Law and the Narcotics Problem", *Journal of Criminal Law, Criminology and Police Science*, Vol. 51, No. 5 (Jan.-Feb. 1961) pp. 512—527.

Castle Peak Drug Addiction Treatment Centre. *Annual Report* (Various years).

Cattell, S. H. *Health, Welfare and Social Organization in Chinatown, New York City* (New York, Community Service Society, 1962).

Chien, M. N., and J. Lawn. *The Process of Intake, Rehabilitation and Discharge of Treated Addicts* (Hong Kong, S.A.R.D.A., 1963).

Cloward, R. A., and L. E. Ohlin *Delinquency and Opportunity: A Theory of Delinquent Gangs* (New York, Free Press of Glencoe, 1960).

Collis, M. *Foreign Mud: Being an Account of the Opium Imbroglio at Canton in the 1830's and the Anglo-Chinese War that Followed* (New York, Knopf, 1947).

Committee to Consider the Colony's Position with Regard to the Obligations Incurred under the International Opium Convention, 1912. *Report* (Hong Kong, Government Printer, 1924).

Criminal Statistics: Standard Classification of Offences. United Nations, E/CN.5/ 337 (1959).

Dangerous Drugs. Ordinance and Subsidiary Legislation. No. 134 of the Revised Edition, 1950 (Hong Kong, Government Printer, n.d.) (And amendments).

Ebin, D. (ed.). *The Drug Experience: First-Person Accounts of Addicts, Writers, Scientists and Others* (New York, Orion Press, 1961).

Elridge, W. B. *Narcotics and the Law: A Critique of the American Experiment in Narcotic Drug Control* (Chicago: American Bar Foundation, 1957).

Endacott, G. B. *A History of Hong Kong* (London, Oxford University Press, 1958).

Fort, J. "Narcotics: The International Picture", *California Youth Authority Quarterly*, Vol. 14, No. 2 (Summer 1961), pp. 3—17.

Fu, Shang-Ling. *Statistical Report on the Sample Survey of Prostitutes in Hong*

---

* For news items see the footnotes.

Kong: Submitted to the Sub-Committee of Moral Welfare, Social Welfare Advisory Committee, Government of Hong Kong (Hong Kong: n.p., c. 1955).

Gavit, J. P. *Opium* (New York, Brentano's, 1927).

Gould, R. *China in the Sun* (New York, Doubleday, 1946).

Hennessy, J. P. "Despatches between Governor J. Pope Hennessy and the Earl of Carnarvon, Principal Secretary of State for the Colonies", Nos. 32, 39, 45, 122 of June 30, 1877, *Hong Kong Gazette*, June 11, 1881, pp. 455—458.

Hong Kong Census Commissioner (K. M. A. Barnett). *Hong Kong Report on the 1961 Census.* 3 vols (Hong Kong, Government Printer, 1962).

Hong Kong Colonial Surgeon. "Report for 1891", *Papers Laid before the Legislative Council of Hong Kong.* 1892. No. 30/92, pp. 391—452.

Hong Kong Commissioner of Police. *Annual Departmental Report* (Various years).

Hong Kong Commissioner of Prisons. *Annual Departmental Report* (Various years).

Hong Kong Commissioner of Resettlement. *Annual Departmental Report* (Various years).

Hong Kong Department of Labour. *Annual Departmental Report* (Various years).

Hong Kong Director of Commerce and Industry. *Annual Departmental Report* (Various years).

Hong Kong Director of Social Welfare. *Annual Departmental Report* (Various years).

Hong Kong Discharged Prisoners' Aid Society. *Annual General Meeting: Chairman's Report.* (Various years).

Hong Kong Discharged Prisoners' Aid Society. *Quarterly Newsletter* (Various issues).

Hong Kong Discharged Prisoners' Aid Society. Chief Welfare Officer. *Report* (Various periods).

Hong Kong Discharged Prisoners' Aid Society. *Statistical Report* (Various years).

Hong Kong Drug Addicts Treatment and Rehabilitation Ordinance, No. 34 of 1960 (Hong Kong, Government Printer, c. 1960).

Hong Kong Government. *Hong Kong Report for the Year 1960* (Hong Kong, Government Press, 1961) (And similar reports for other years).

Hong Kong Government. *The Problem of Narcotic Use in Hong Kong: A White Paper Laid before Legislative Council 11th November, 1959* (Hong Kong, Government Printer, 1959).

Hong Kong Government. *A Problem of People* (Hong Kong, Government Printer, 1960).

Hong Kong Government. *Report .. on the Traffic in Opium and Dangerous Drugs* (Various years).

Hong Kong Governor. "Memorandum Regarding the Restriction of Opium in Hong Kong and China", *Sessional Papers*, 1909, No. 3/09, pp. 25—40.

Hong Kong Narcotics Advisory Committee. *Progress Report 1959/60* (Hong Kong, Government Printer, c. 1961).

Hong Kong Prisons Ordinance, No. 17 of 1954 (Hong Kong, Government Printer, n.d.).

Hong Kong Prisons. *Prison Rules* (Hong Kong, 1954).

Hong Kong Prisons. *Standing Orders* (Hong Kong, n.d.).

Hong Kong Secretary for Chinese Affairs. *Annual Departmental Report* (Various years).

Hong Kong Secretary for Chinese Affairs. *Anti-Narcotics Campaign. S.C.A.'s Appeal to Every Government Servant for Help.* (Editions in Chinese and English) (Hong Kong, 1960).

Hong Kong Secretary for Chinese Affairs. [Three anti-narcotics leaflets in Chinese]. (Hong Kong, c. 1960).

Hong Kong Standing Committee and Advisory Committee on Corruption. *Reports* (Hong Kong, Government Printer, 1962).

Hong Kong Supreme Court. Registrar. *Annual Departmental Report* (Various years).

"Hong Kong's Prison for Drug Addicts", *Bulletin on Narcotics,* Vol. 13 No. 1 (Jan.-March 1961), pp. 13—20.

"Hsiang-K'ang Ya-pien hui-i lu (Reminiscenses on Opium in Hong Kong)", *Hsiang-K'ang Chih-nan* (Hong Kong, Far East News Agency, 1948), pp. 18—19.

Illicit Traffic - Hong Kong: Statement by the Delegation of the United Kingdom of Great Britain and Northern Ireland to the United Nations for the Eighteenth Session of the Commission on Narcotics. United Nations, E/CN.7/L.262 (1963).

The Illicit Traffic in Narcotics Drugs in South-East Asia. United Nations, E/CN.7/440 (1963).

Incidence of Drug Addiction. United Nations, E/CN.7/439 (1963).

Joint Committee of the American Bar Association and the American Medical Association. *Drug Addiction: Crime or Disease?* (Bloomington, Ind., Indiana University Press, 1961).

Jones, J. *The Mysteries of Opium Reveal'd.* (London, R. Smith, 1701).

Kao, L. M. (ed.). *Hong Kong* (Kowloon: East Arts Company, 1961).

Karnow, S. "The Opium Must Go Through", *Life,* Vol. 55, No. 9 (August 30, 1963), pp. 11—12.

Kolb, L., and A. G. du Mez. *The Prevalence and Trend of Drug Addiction in the United States and Factors Influencing It* (Washinghon, D.C., Government Printing Office, 1924).

Larimore, G., and H. Brill. "The British Narcotic System: Report of Study", *New York State Journal of Medicine,* Vol. 60 (January 1, 1960), pp. 107—115.

Lindesmith, A. R. "The British System of Narcotics Control", *Law and Contemporary Problems,* Vol. 22 (Winter 1957), pp. 138—154.

Lutheran World Federation. *General Background Information on Hong Kong* (Hong Kong, 1963).

Lutheran World Federation. *Report* (Various periods).

Lutheran World Service. [Leaflet on the Pui Sun Fraternal Association] (Hong Kong, c. 1963).

Lutheran World Service. *Project for the After-Care of Narcotic Addicts* (Hong Kong, 1962).

MacMurray, J. V. A. *Treaties and Agreements with and Concerning China, 1894—1919* (New York, Oxford University Press, 1921).

Morgan, W. P. *Triad Societies in Hong Kong* (Hong Kong, Government Press, 1960).

Morgan, W. P. "The Work of the Police Force in Hong Kong", *Corona,* Vol. 14, No. 9 (Sept. 1962), pp. 329—333.

New York State Division of Parole. *An Experiment in the Supervision of Paroled Offenders Addicted to Narcotic Drugs. Final Report of the Special Narcotic Project.* Prep. by M. H. Diskind *et al.* (c. 1960).

Norton-Kyshe, J. M. *The History of the Laws and Courts of Hong Kong.* 2 vols. (London, T. Fisher Unwin, 1898).

Perkins, D. "William Henry Seward", *Dictionary of American Bibliography.* Vol. 16 (New York, Scribner's, 1935), pp. 615—621.

Pillai, K. S. C. "The Puff of Ruin", *Far Eastern Economic Review,* Vol. 41, No. 12, pp. 759—764.

Roy, Andrew T. *On Asia's Rim* (New York, Friendship Press, 1962).

Rubin, S. *Crime and Juvenile Delinquency* 2nd ed. (New York, Oceana, 1961).

Schur, E. M. *Narcotic Addiction in Britain and America: The Impact of Public Policy* (Bloomington, Ind., Indiana University Press, 1962).

Seward, O. R. (ed.). *William H. Seward's Travels around the World* (New York, Appleton and Co., 1873).

Smith, George. *A Narrative of the Exploratory Visit to Each of the Consular Cities of China, and to the Islands of Hong Kong and Chusan* (New York, Harper and Brothers, 1847).

Society for the Aid and Rehabilitation of Drug Addicts. Aftercare Service. *Follow Up and Aftercare Report No. 1.* (Hong Kong, 1964).

Society for the Aid and Rehabilitation of Drug Addicts. *Shek Kwu Chau Centre Opened by H. E. the Governor .. on 23rd April, 1963.* (Hong Kong, 1963).

Storey, R. J. "Courts and Prisons in the Far East", *The Magistrate,* Vol. 18, No. 4 (April 1962), pp. 44—46.

Superintendent of H.M. Prison (Tai Lam). *Report for Period Ending 30th September, 1960.*

United Kingdom Ministry of Health. Department of Health for Scotland. *Drug Addiction: Report of the Interdepartmental Committee* (London, H.M.S.O., 1961).

United Nations Commission on Narcotic Drugs. *Report of the Sixteenth Session.* United Nations, E/3512-E/CN.7/411 (1961).

United States Treasury Department. Bureau of Narcotics. *Traffic in Opium and Other Dangerous Drugs for the Year Ended December 31, 1943: Report* (Washington, D.C., Government Printing Office, 1944).

United States Treasury Department. Advisory Committee to the Federal Bureau of Narcotics. *Comments on Narcotic Drugs: Interim Report of the Joint Committee of the American Bar Association and the American Medical Association on Narcotic Drugs* (Washington, D.C., 1958).

Wagner, R. F. *Remarks by Mayor Robert F. Wagner at the White House Conference on Narcotics* (Press Release, September 27, 1962).

Waley, A. *The Opium War through Chinese Eyes* (London, Allen and Unwin, 1958).

Way, E. L. *Control and Treatment of Drug Addiction in Hong Kong.* Paper presented at the Narcotics Conference held at the University of California at Los Angeles, April 27—28, 1963.

White House *Ad Hoc* Panel on Drug Abuse. *Progress Report* (Washington, D.C., 1962).

Wood, W. A. *A Brief History of Hong Kong* (Hong Kong, South China Morning Post, c. 1940).

Zusman, J. "A Brief History of the Narcotics Control Controversy", *Mental Hygiene,* Vol. 45, No. 3 (1961), pp. 383—388.

INDEX